Handbook for Total Quality Assurance

Complete Management Library

Volume XXVI

Edward M. Stiles

Quality Assurance Manager
Olivetti-Underwood Corp.
Hartford, Conn.

HANDBOOK FOR TOTAL QUALITY ASSURANCE

National Foremen's Institute
Bureau of Business Practice
National Sales Development Institute
Waterford, Connecticut

COMPLETE MANAGEMENT LIBRARY
VOLUME XXVI

LIBRARY OF CONGRESS CATALOG CARD NUMBER 64-22218

PRINTED IN THE UNITED STATES OF AMERICA

Ninth Printing, October, 1969

TABLE OF CONTENTS

CHAPTER ONE

What Is Quality?

Consumers, purchasing agents and government procurement officers are now demanding more quality for their money. When they do not receive the quality they require they show no hesitancy in switching to another line or an entirely different product. When they receive it, sales increase dramatically as, for example, when Chrysler Corporation increased its engines' power train components warranty for five years or 50,000 miles. In the past few years, customer demands have given quality a commanding position it lacked before.

This accent on quality creates the biggest problem facing the executive today. With overcapacity in many product lines at home and under tremendous international competitive pressures, he cannot pass on to his customers higher costs incurred to improve quality. At the same time he has precious little margin for absorbing the higher cost himself.

Quality may be the key word in any manager's future. Competitive quality demands in the years ahead will tax the capacity of each business to perform at peak efficiency. For the individual manager, this requires nothing less than his best effort and performance to survive. There will be no margin of error for lax or shoddy work, by any one, at any level, in any company.

The crucial nature of this quality problem was bluntly expressed by a leading businessman: "In my experience . . . I find it difficult to find any high-quality goods in consumer products. I think that we are in grave danger of losing what we had many years ago, when our artisans took personal pride in the reliability and quality of their product . . ."[1]

This is not an isolated criticism of the quality and reliability of today's products. Admiral Hyman G. Rickover's harsh comments on the quality level of nuclear submarine components and the National Aeronautic and Space Administration reports of astronaut experiences with space capsule quality failures received wide publicity in the early 1960's. Popular writers scored American industry for poor quality and shoddy products.

Management must overcome this adverse publicity and meet these demands, improving the quality reputations of their companies in the process, or perish. A program is urgently required to insure that only satisfactory products are delivered to the customer, and that these products will perform as promised for the required length of time at a reasonable cost. Japan presents a prime example of what can be done in a determined effort to improve the quality reputation of products. Prior to World War II, "Made in Japan" was a synonym for shoddy, cheap, and almost useless goods. Today, after sweeping efforts by the government, trade associations, and private businesses, Japan leads the world in producing the "best" in many product lines, ranging through such diverse fields as locomotives, optical equipment, and ships.

Trends in Quality Demands

This tremendous surge in quality demands in industry is the composite result of these trends:

Customers are demanding more complex equipment to perform a greater variety of functions with better reliability and

[1] Edward A. McCreary, "Executive Trends," *Nation's Business*, April, 1962, p. 14.

lowered service requirements. The automatic washer-drier has supplanted the wringer-type washing machine and the open-air clothes line. Cameras today are equipped with coupled range-finders and automatic shutters. Lawn mowers have semiautomatic starters in place of the length of rope and pulley formerly standard on such small gasoline engines.

The general level of technology is rising rapidly. Automation of production processes, advances in materials, and greatly increased design sophistication all contribute to this surge.

Costs are soaring. Business faces a serious squeeze between increasing costs and prices fixed by customer resistance. This produces two distinct pressures on quality.

1. The greater the push exerted by total costs, the more vigorous are the measures taken by management to reduce them. Such measures usually lead to increased mechanization and automation and place more critical demands on quality.

2. The drive to reduce costs sharpens accounting systems, and results in better identification of quality costs. Many concerns have been shocked to find that their total quality bill exceeded 10 per cent of gross sales. Other concerns still don't know what their quality costs are, although they may be equally high. Such quality costs, if not identified and reduced, result in the difference between profit and loss.

As these trends develop, increasing statistical sophistication has given industry a clearer, grimmer picture of the tangible results of customer dissatisfaction with product quality. A leading appliance manufacturer estimates that one in three dissatisfied customers complains to the company, but that each advertises his gripe to 15 friends and acquaintances. This means 45 potential lost sales for every letter of complaint. One of the big three auto makers has one case on record where the angry owner of a luxury car cost 100 lost sales in one year. A giant food processor calculates 500 bad cans of food are behind each written complaint they receive on poor quality.

Development of Quality Techniques

From the day it opened its doors for business every company has utilized techniques of one kind or another for handling customer quality demands. In the nineteenth century, shop supervisors were responsible in a very personal sense for the quality of the products they produced. The foreman was often the only man who was capable of making a measurement or who knew what to check. He kept his standards under his cast-iron derby, interpreted the crude blueprints for his people, and determined what would or would not leave the shop as finished goods.

Factories grew in size and complexity through the years. The line organization multiplied. Frederick Taylor developed the concepts of scientific management at the turn of the twentieth century. One of these concepts was that inspection was a specialized function, different from production work. The inspector appeared on the factory floor, reporting to the line foreman, with the responsibility for sorting the bad from the good prior to delivery.

The number of inspectors grew and the inspection supervisory function appeared. Foremen, general foremen of inspection and chief inspectors appeared on the scene. The realization that inspection should be separated from production management spread, and the head of inspection began to report to the works manager level or above, independently of the line production organization. This represented the ultimate development of what Paul Clifford defined as *inspection quality control.* Its fundamental responsibility is the protection of producer and consumer against shipment of bad product. Typically, the job does not extend beyond the shop floor. Analysis and feedback of inspection data for corrective action is usually limited. In most applications, the need to find mistakes before large quantities of scrap and rework are produced has forced adoption of some sort of in-process inspection. Cost pressures have also been instrumental in forcing the adoption of statistical techniques, to reduce the amount of inspection required.

It is evident that *inspection quality control* is a great improvement over older inspection systems. It has saved industry a vast amount of money and has contributed to customer satisfaction. Even today, many industries would benefit greatly if they adopted this concept. To mention a few examples, the average foundry, die caster, and garment producer have yet to progress to this point.

Concurrently with the growth of inspection quality control in the 1920's and 1930's, a new field opened up as statistical quality control techniques were developed and applied to industrial activities. It was realized that the analysis of machine and tool capabilities, sampling tables and techniques, design of experiments, and other procedures could predict and influence product quality. Pushed by its pioneer developers in Bell Laboratories, *statistical quality control* spread through certain areas of industry. It was based on the principle that the reason for inspection was the presence of unreliable variations in the manufacturing process. Statistical methods were used to study these variations and determine the quality levels to be expected from these processes. It became generally recognized that good inspection did not guarantee good quality. Some statistical techniques, principally sampling inspection practices, were incorporated into regular inspection operations. World War II, with its development of government inspection requirements, hastened this marriage of statistical quality control with inspection quality control.

This was an uneasy union. Statistical quality control was labeled as esoteric, abstract, and unrealistic by people who did not understand statistics. Courses in statistics were foisted upon unresponsive shop personnel. Frequently the statistician's approach was: "When I have taught you what I know, you will then realize why it is necessary for you to learn what I am teaching you." This attitude was not easily accepted by tough-minded, result-oriented line managers. At the same time, statisticians found their new approach to quality control ineffective. The American Society for Quality Control had defined quality control as the practical application to industrial problems of the science of statistics. True, statistics could measure the extent and determine the nature of a problem. However, statistics *per se* would not make the problem disappear. This required positive action by people other than statisticians.

Because of this situation, a new concept developed in the

1950's. Its principal spokesman was Dr. A. V. Feigenbaum, of the General Electric Company, who defined this approach as *total quality control* which is:

"An effective system for integrating the quality-development, quality-maintenance, and quality-improvement efforts of the various groups in an organization so as to enable production and service at the most economical levels which allow for full customer satisfaction." [2]

This concept recognizes that quality control efforts start with the design of the product and end only when the customer remains satisfied while using the product. Its objective is to make the product right the first time. Defects are to be prevented so that routine inspection can be reduced or eliminated. Feigenbaum divides this task into four main elements:

1. *new-design control*
2. *incoming material control*
3. *product control*
4. *special process studies.*

Each element is viewed as an activity of a quality control engineering group. This group will measure and analyze the efforts of others in the organization, point out errors, and provide information for corrective action. In short, remnants of the old inspection philosophy of "they shall not pass" are applied to all company functions affecting the product. This is the great weakness of this concept.

There is another weakness inherent in the statistical approach used in most quality control programs. People are subtly conditioned to believe they cannot do a perfect job and will make errors. They assume that they are allowed a certain percentage of error. Statistical concepts of process capability have embraced the view that the process is never perfect and will produce some bad items. In fact, the nomenclature of quality control uses "nice" words to soften the impact of failure. There are no *bad* or *no*

[2] A. V. Feigenbaum, *Total Quality Control* (New York: McGraw-Hill Book Company, Inc.), p. 1.

good or *lousy* parts. Instead, they are *discrepant* or *defective* or *vary*. Statements about *quality levels* are weasel-worded with expressions of *confidence levels* concerning *firm positions*.

Your personal experiences will show you that this bland acceptance of mistakes is not rational. When is the last time you forgot to pay your income tax? If your pay check is short, do you accept the shortage as one of those "normal" mistakes a company makes? When did you last go to work on a Sunday because you forgot the plant was closed?

Mistakes are avoidable. They are usually caused by lack of attention. In fact, cannot errors committed measure the value a man places on specific actions? Even if errors result from accidents, why does the man on the spot fail to note that the accident occurred and to report it? Lack of interest? Failure to identify with the job? How can any responsible manager accept such attitudes as irremedial elements in the business?

Total Quality Assurance

What is the solution? The obvious key is to move the emphasis from total quality *control* to total quality *assurance*. The National Aeronautics and Space Administration defines *quality assurance* as *"a planned and systematic pattern of all actions necessary to provide adequate confidence that the end items will perform satisfactorily in actual operations."* [3] The emphasis is not on control. Instead, all actions are to be performed properly the first time to produce a final product that meets a predetermined quality level.

Total quality assurance is not a neat package of functions assigned to a specific organizational entity. It is a broad set of policies applied by all managers in the company, with the service assistance of a staff function charged with policy development and administration in quality matters. A degree of control naturally follows on a line-staff relationship.

[3] Ralph von Osinski, "Control—From Conception to Customer," *Quality Assurance*, May, 1963, p. 26.

Four broad functions make up total quality assurance in all areas of the firm:

1. **Determination of the desired quality level of the design,** product, processes, and procedures.
2. **Determination of the actual quality of raw materials,** product in process, and finished goods as compared to desired and specified quality levels.
3. **Determination of optimum economic quality obtainable** under existing conditions as compared to the desired quality level, and initiation of action calculated to attain this optimum.
4. **Action to improve actual quality** and productivity levels and reduce costs by influencing designs, specifications, processes, and procedures.

These are functions in which every element of the company, from president to production worker, participate. They are the basis of all work performed by any employee in any business. They are not the exclusive province of a quality control engineering group or statistical department.

Future Development

The day is rapidly approaching when our larger corporations will have vice presidents in charge of quality assurance. These men will have the same relationship to quality control that vice presidents of finance have to accounting. It will be a major subordinate function under their immediate control, but it will not be the sole reason for their existence. Their responsibility will include all aspects of quality, and the company's quality failure will be their personal failure. Total quality assurance demands a tough-minded executive at its head who understands that performance is all that matters and his contribution to the company is to assure the delivery of a quality product. As a former President of the United States once said, "If you can't stand the heat, get out of the kitchen."

Listen to an angry man, Mr. P. B. Crosby of the Martin Company:

> I've been in the quality control business for a good many years. During that time I've been fortunate enough to be exposed to practically every phase of the profession, from inspection to management. I have attended many symposiums, sat in on innumerable bull sessions in hotels, saloons, airplanes, and offices. I have heard what should be done, what is being done, and what will be done. The information I get is enough to fill one's heart with pride in his chosen work. But, between us girls, most of it is a bunch of baloney!
>
> During the past years I have visited almost every type of industry and talked to the quality people responsible for running the operation. I have then talked to the people performing the jobs and investigated the systems myself. Believe me, there is a difference.
>
> For some unknown reason, it is becoming fashionable to divorce the quality control activities from such unglamorous activities as inspection, test, and shipping. Always there is a program "just being developed" which will solve the company's quality problems and always there is a dusty book of Quality Procedures which has been "signed off by the customer."
>
> Quality control has become a significant part of industry today, yet our product quality is deteriorating. The pendulum has swung from a period of each man being responsible for his own work to a period of statistical controls which no one understands except the quality control people. Somewhere in between is an area full of opportunity. This area is one where prevention of defects is a fact and every quality control man knows his job. Nothing is left to chance . . .
>
> Quality managers across the country are responsible for the general reduction of quality in our products. Having won the fight for recognition of q.c. as a science, they are now engrossed in being members of the "team." This results in a gradual changing of what was once black or white into various shades of gray. Rationalization is our downfall.
>
> Let's go back to making it like the print. Let's stand firm with engineering, manufacturing, and procurement early in the game. Make them state what they want, be sure it's what they need—then hold them to it. Don't let them compromise; don't stand for marginal equipment.
>
> In short—get off the "team." Quit helping them violate their own standards. We'll be less popular and we'll probably have restless nights—but we'll be producing quality products.[4]

[4] P. B. Crosby, Letter to the Editor, *Quality Assurance*, August, 1963, p. 6.

Total quality assurance is a tremendous challenge to all managers. Business survival in the future will depend on a firm's quality image, as established by product performance, not advertising "puff." It is the job of every manager to build this image for his company.

CHAPTER TWO

Scope and Objectives

Determining the scope of total quality assurance is top management's job. The president must actually determine if there will be a total quality assurance program in his company, and must set the pace the program will follow. If he does not actively participate in this manner, there will be no program, for the broad scope of total quality assurance makes it impossible for a subordinate executive to launch a successful program. In making this determination, two fundamental requisites must be considered:

1. Top management must establish a quality philosophy, set quality targets, and organize the company to reach these targets.
2. Top management must make sure that it puts its quality philosophy across to all employees, at all levels.

Total quality assurance is an across-the-board, company-wide activity. It starts with marketing and an evaluation of the quality level customers want and will pay for. Research and development produces ideas and concepts which engineering refines to exact specifications to determine design quality. Purchasing selects suppliers to furnish parts and materials of specified quality. Industrial engineering determines tools and processes for manufacturing, guided by the quality levels desired. Manufacturing produces a product of a specific quality, verified by inspection and test, to meet engineering specifications. Packaging, shipping, and traffic determine the state of product quality upon arrival at the customer. Sales and service affect the customer's satisfactory use of the product.

Plans Must Be Custom Tailored

Every company at any particular point in time has its own particular "personality" and individuality in its approach to its business. Thus, a total quality assurance program must be tailored to fit the organization which will use it.

Take a look at the budget systems used in most companies today. The controller, or someone in an equivalent position, sets up certain broad rules and regulations within which all managers are expected to operate. A particular manager knows how much he can spend for labor, equipment, supplies, repairs, training, travel, and any other factors which fall within his jurisdiction. If he deviates from his budget, he must answer for it to both his immediate superior and the controller. However, budget rules and regulations differ from one company to another. So do the particular factors or accounts in a given manager's budget.

The quality plan and its supporting systems must be adapted to the company's operating patterns in the same manner as the budget system. A successful plan at ABC Corporation cannot blindly be adopted by the management of XYZ Company. The quality plan must integrate and delegate quality authority. There must also be an auditing or control system to insure that the plan is adhered to and produces the desired results.

Objectives of Quality Assurance Organization

Within a company, a specific group of people is held responsible for planning, auditing, and controlling quality. They may be called inspection, quality verification, quality control, quality assurance, etc. Regardless of identification, the group's management has two basic objectives:

1. To contribute to the maintenance of business income and to an increase in sales revenues and return on invested capital.
2. To provide a genuine sense of accomplishment, for those who conduct the quality assurance program, through activities relating primarily to product quality rather than to some other business function, such as sales, research, production, or finance.

The success of a quality assurance program depends on how well these objectives are met. An unsuccessful quality program is one which does not meet both of these objectives, does not satisfy the management of the business, and will ultimately lead to personnel changes in the quality assurance area.

Briefly, the immediate objectives of the quality assurance group are to accomplish two tasks:

1. Find out what top management wants from quality and satisfy those wants as completely as possible.
2. Educate top management to accept those objectives that the quality assurance activity believes should be the target in quality areas. This cannot be attempted until quality assurance has won management's confidence and support by successful performance of the first task.

Analyzing Objectives All companies are run to make money, or, if nonprofit, not to lose money. However, almost every company has auxiliary objectives. Quality assurance operations must mesh with these secondary objectives and assist in attaining them. To take a specific case, a manufacturer of business machines had the following objectives, all calculated to increase profitability:

1. *To increase its share of its market 10 per cent per year.*
2. *To increase sales of one specific product 25 per cent per year.*

3. *To maintain product prices at existing levels, absorbing wage and material cost increases without increasing product costs and prices.*

After analysis, the manufacturing vice president of this company arrived at the following objectives for the factory organization as a whole:

1. Produce machines at a quality level that would assure a 50 per cent reduction in installation time at the customer's facility and in service requirements during the warranty period.
2. Cut factory operating costs 4 per cent per month.
3. Strengthen and complete management staffing of the factory organization.
4. Revise and make major advances in assembly methods and techniques for two principal product lines.

The quality assurance operation then established its objectives, all of which supported one or more of the manufacturing or corporate objectives:

1. Work with other operations to reduce scrap and rework charges 44 per cent during the next ten months.
2. Complete installation of a reliability testing program in the next eight months.
3. Reduce inspection costs 4 per cent per month without affecting product quality.
4. Install a quality incentive plan in the assembly operations within one year.
5. Increase repair labor performed in the salvage department by transferring 50 per cent of repair work then performed by manufacturing direct labor.
6. Develop and maintain a quality specification book on each product.

Each of these objectives had specific dates or targets to be met. Each was supported by a detailed program that outlined step by step the measures necessary to meet each objective. Target dates were set and reported on monthly for each step. These were not *paper objectives,* but carefully thought-out targets, whose attainment would improve specific aspects of the company's business. At each organizational level, the objectives selected meshed smoothly with the aims of top management and those of other operations in the firm.

Thus far there has been no mention of total quality assurance or total quality control as a specific objective of the quality organization. The reason is simple. In the total quality assurance concept, with its insistence on company-wide quality actions by all organizational components which can affect quality of the product, no one group can carve out as its objective the creation of total quality orientation and control. Professional quality control people should be grateful for the work done to organize, document, and publicize the total quality concepts. Many people in the profession have recognized the need for an organized development of this concept; some have even practiced its principles; but few have endeavored to sell total quality concepts in a package presentable to all members of management. In the past few years, many companies have adopted Dr. Feigenbaum's concepts of total *quality control,* but few companies have attained total *quality assurance.*

In particular, many quality operations have experienced severe frustrations in attempting new design control, as outlined by Feigenbaum. It has proved almost impossible in these companies to obtain acceptance from the various engineering groups for new design "control." The announcement that such "control" is an objective of the quality organization is an almost certain guarantee that the desired control will not be achieved.

The *total quality assurance concept* puts its major emphasis on planning for quality by each activity, with the quality assurance activity serving as a service function to advise on past problems and recommend or suggest methods of avoiding such problems in new products. Quality assurance wants to spark quality approaches by each person to his job. Quality assurance objectives are not confined to one area of the company, but should be included in every activity's list of objectives.

Limits of Authority and Responsibility

Two aspects of initiating a total quality assurance program may have a disturbing influence on management. Such programs, no matter how skillfully presented as service functions to assist other managers in the quality aspects of their operations, may arouse responses similar to the following:

1. **"Quality Assurance is second-guessing me and is not a creative group.** It looks like all they do is to criticize us and try to publicize the lousy job they claim we are doing."
2. **"Quality Assurance is continually looking over our shoulders and trying to tell us how to run our operations."**

These responses, particularly from technical people, are going to exist, whether they are openly expressed or secretly discussed in closed sessions among small groups. Let's be honest about the basic approach used in any inspection, quality control, or quality assurance operation. It operates by finding mistakes, determining who made them, and attempting to get the responsible party to correct his actions. Unless carefully and tactfully done, this can become a destructive force in the organization.

The philosophy of modern quality control techniques is that 100 per cent inspection is inefficient, expensive, and wasteful. Further, quality control people insist that it is essential that the operator be held totally responsible for the quality of his work. Yet, in attempting to apply total quality control concepts, many people have reverted back to the police force approach in starting a program of new design control.

Is it necessary to constantly look over the shoulder of the designers and other technical people to insure they do not err? If so, since quality control people are also technical people, which activity is looking over their shoulders? If no one is, should someone be assigned to the job?

In this area of total quality approaches, the engineering groups must know that quality assurance services are always available.

Further, management should spell out Engineering's obligation to consult with Quality Assurance on quality considerations. One of Quality Assurance's major functions is to provide such service through the quality engineering group. If Engineering does not use good judgment, Quality Assurance operations on the pilot run and in reliability testing should be sharp enough to find the quality problems and point them out to engineering people. This constant feedback, in a firm but tactful manner without excessive publicity, will highlight the need for closer liaison between Quality Assurance and the engineers. If special studies or experiments are required, Quality Assurance should be responsible for pointing out this need to its engineering partners and assist in obtaining it for them.

In establishing quality assurance objectives, some criteria for establishing the scope of each activity's program must be developed. The simplest criteria is to test each proposed program and project by asking: *Does it add value?* In other words, if a proposal does not contribute to profit, or assist some other activity in contributing to profit, why consider it?

The second question is: *Should Quality Assurance do it?* Quality assurance people must face up to reality and admit they are not Jacks-of-all-trades. They have certain special skills, tools, and techniques. If the proposal does not require these special abilities, or if some other group has superior abilities, why should Quality Assurance do it? Quality Assurance cannot muscle in on activities which are the legitimate and assigned responsibilities of other operations. On the other hand, Quality Assurance should not become the garbage can into which other areas drop their unwanted functions. In such cases, rather than attempting to take on the job itself, Quality Assurance must devise approaches which will motivate the responsible group to take up its unwanted and unappreciated task.

If a certain activity belongs to Quality Assurance and is required to meet corporate goals, good! Do it! If total quality assurance is better attained if someone else does the job, equally good! Let them, or persuade them, to do it! Don't rock the corporate boat, and destroy reputations, by futile empire building in quality assurance operations.

Need for Modification and Innovation

It has been pointed out that a business organization has an almost human personality, and it alters and changes as time passes and personnel come and go. These changes affect the objectives of an organization and the manner in which objectives are attained. Quality plans must be modified and objectives revised in response to these changes.

To be realistic, an organization can attack only a limited number of objectives at any one time. Fragmenting efforts among many objectives merely insures that few or none will be attained. The average executive is doing very well if, in addition to conducting day-to-day operations, he works on five to seven specific objectives. As each objective is reached, a new one should be set up in its place.

Innovation is constantly at work, affecting quality plans like any others. Such diverse factors as automation, changes in sales methods and salesmen compensation, advances in data processing, and new union contracts all force continuous modification of the objectives of quality assurance operations. The quality assurance organization cannot stagnate. It must be alert to such innovations as they appear and incorporate them at the fastest desirable rate in quality assurance operations and objectives.

CHAPTER THREE

Administration

Administration of the quality assurance operation, more than any other industrial management assignment, depends on the maturity and effectiveness of the individual who heads up the quality activity. His job is to reduce quality cost, increase the company's profit, and increase sales demands for the product. His entire operation depends upon the skillful handling of the three fundamental operating assumptions of every quality activity which are:

1. The assumption that information furnished by inspection is accurate and reliable.
2. The assumption that information furnished by inspection is processed with sufficient speed to prevent deterioration.
3. The realization that no quality assurance employee implements action to improve quality *himself,* but must persuade some other person to take the desired action.

The size of the company, types of products and processes, degrees of manufacturing complexity, and other factors affect the administration of a quality assurance department. However, six steps are essential to achieve maximum efficiency. These are:

1. *Organizing the quality assurance department.*
2. *Planning quality assurance activities.*
3. *Directing quality assurance activities.*
4. *Controlling quality assurance results.*
5. *Appraising departmental performance.*
6. *Improving departmental effectiveness.*

In considering the administration of a quality assurance department, it is important to survey all company-wide operations to insure the proper integration of quality assurance goals, plans, and programs with the objectives of the corporate whole. There have been numerous quality installations where the objectives of the quality manager diverged from those of the organization as a whole. Top management does not long tolerate such a situation. Either the quality manager's outlook or the quality manager is changed, and quickly!

The component parts of the quality assurance departmental plans and programs must be interwoven so that all activities mesh precisely and harmoniously, not only within the quality assurance department but with other groups as well. The finest sampling plan can be developed as an in-process control measure in a factory, but unless sufficient clerical time is available to handle the data the plan produces and the quality control engineer has sold the plan to manufacturing supervision, the inspection effort in checking the samples is wasted.

Principles of Organization

In organizing a quality assurance operation the following principles should be considered:

1. Basic quality responsibility rests in the hands of top management, who must acknowledge and accept the responsibility.

2. The first responsibility of Quality Assurance is to assure the

quality of the company's product. The second is to assist in assuring the optimum reduction in the costs of obtaining this quality.

3. The key to a successful quality assurance operation is the fastest possible cycling of the feedback loop:

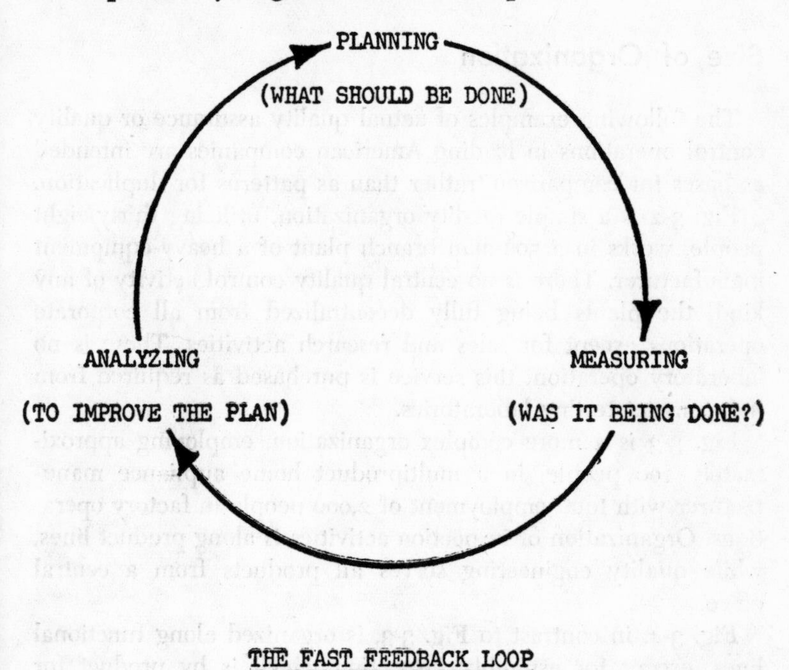

THE FAST FEEDBACK LOOP

Fig. 3-1

4. All components of the loop should be under the direction of Quality Assurance to maximize speed and accuracy and to provide accountability. Quality Assurance should include the inspection and test operations sometimes mistakenly assigned to line manufacturing groups.

5. The key to quality improvement is accurate reporting to management. Quality Assurance needs a short, clear information pipeline to that level of management that can clear up problems and conflicts between Product Engineering, Tooling, Planning, Purchasing, and Manufacturing. These conflicts usually will involve major cost decisions.

6. The guarantee of Quality Assurance is relief from pressure to ship and produce. Quality Assurance should not report to the production superintendent.

Size of Organization

The following examples of actual quality assurance or quality control operations in leading American companies are intended as bases for comparison, rather than as patterns for duplication.

Fig. 3-2 is a simple quality organization, utilizing thirty-eight people, works in a 500-man branch plant of a heavy-equipment manufacturer. There is no central quality control activity of any kind, the plants being fully decentralized from all corporate operations except for sales and research activities. There is no laboratory operation; this service is purchased as required from independent testing laboratories.

Fig. 3-3 is a more complex organization, employing approximately 100 people, in a multiproduct home appliance manufacturer with total employment of 2,000 people in factory operations. Organization of inspection activities is along product lines, while quality engineering serves all products from a central office.

Fig. 3-4, in contrast to Fig. 3-3, is organized along functional lines, except for assembly inspection which is by product for greater familiarity on the part of the inspectors. There are approximately 250 quality assurance employees in this 3,500-man business machine factory.

Fig. 3-5 represents a complex organization involving a central staff and branch operations in each plant to support the multiplant operations of an electronics company. This company believes in strong central control, so that the branch operations receive much greater direction from the corporate director of quality control than would normally be the case. This also creates operating problems, since each branch quality assurance manager has two bosses and seldom succeeds in satisfying both of them.

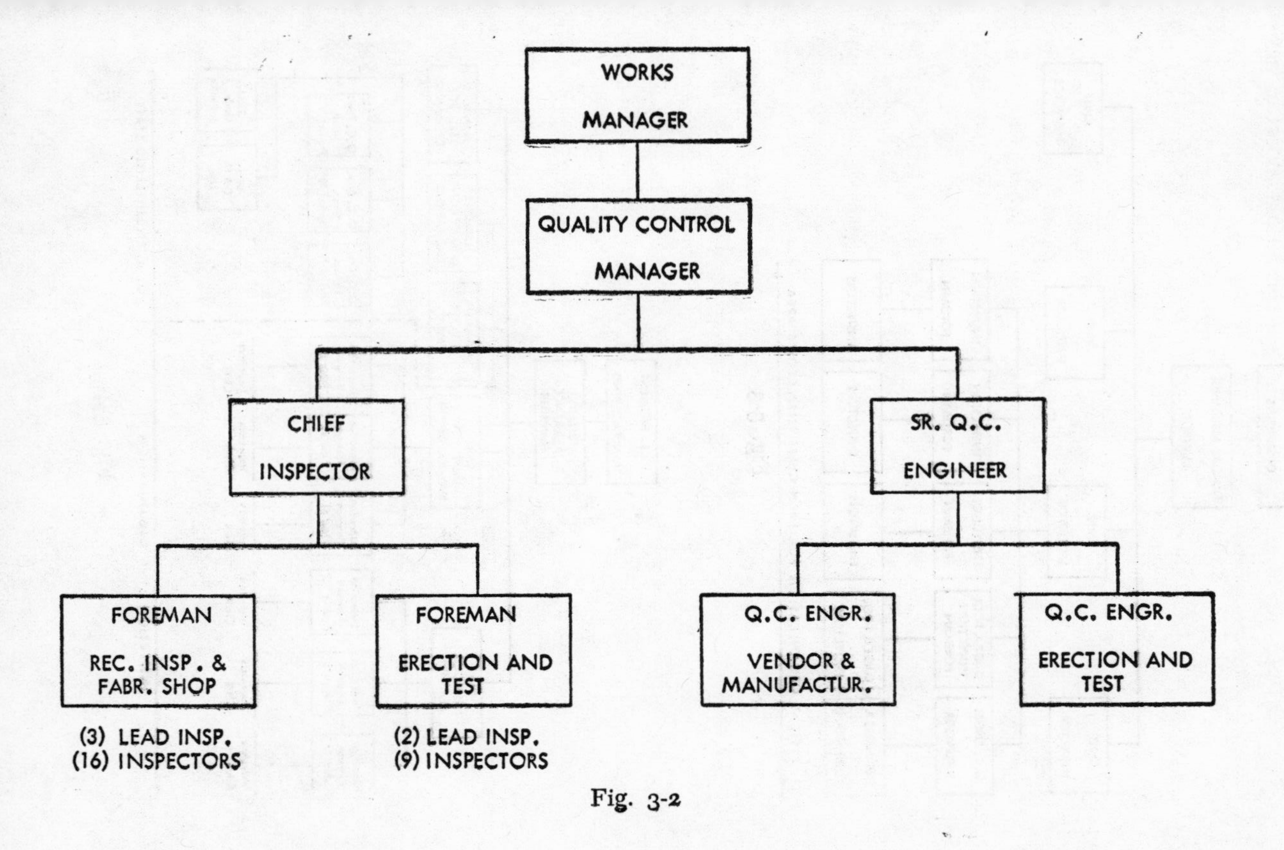
WORKS MANAGER
QUALITY CONTROL MANAGER
CHIEF INSPECTOR
SR. Q.C. ENGINEER
FOREMAN REC. INSP. & FABR. SHOP
(3) LEAD INSP.
(16) INSPECTORS
FOREMAN ERECTION AND TEST
(2) LEAD INSP.
(9) INSPECTORS
Q.C. ENGR. VENDOR & MANUFACTUR.
Q.C. ENGR. ERECTION AND TEST

Fig. 3-2

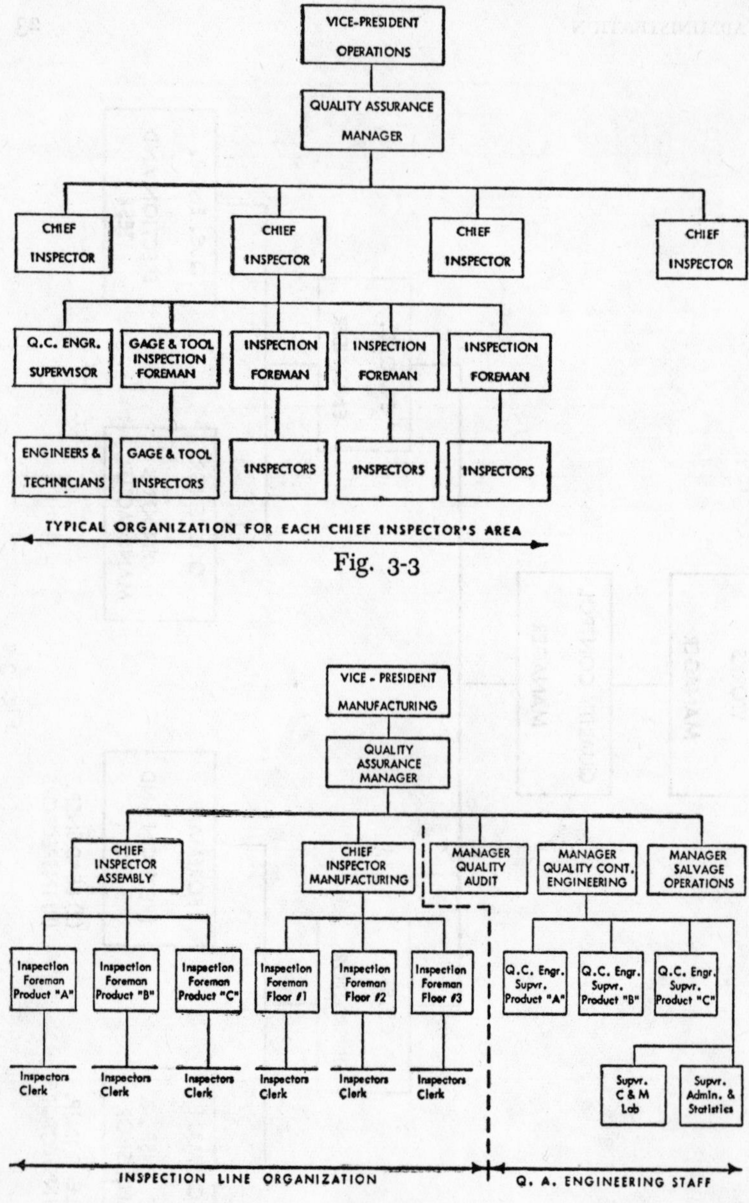
VICE-PRESIDENT OPERATIONS
QUALITY ASSURANCE MANAGER
CHIEF INSPECTOR
CHIEF INSPECTOR
CHIEF INSPECTOR
CHIEF INSPECTOR
Q.C. ENGR. SUPERVISOR
GAGE & TOOL INSPECTION FOREMAN
INSPECTION FOREMAN
INSPECTION FOREMAN
INSPECTION FOREMAN
ENGINEERS & TECHNICIANS
GAGE & TOOL INSPECTORS
INSPECTORS
INSPECTORS
INSPECTORS
TYPICAL ORGANIZATION FOR EACH CHIEF INSPECTOR'S AREA

Fig. 3-3

VICE - PRESIDENT MANUFACTURING
QUALITY ASSURANCE MANAGER
CHIEF INSPECTOR ASSEMBLY
CHIEF INSPECTOR MANUFACTURING
MANAGER QUALITY AUDIT
MANAGER QUALITY CONT. ENGINEERING
MANAGER SALVAGE OPERATIONS
Inspection Foreman Product "A"
Inspection Foreman Product "B"
Inspection Foreman Product "C"
Inspection Foreman Floor #1
Inspection Foreman Floor #2
Inspection Foreman Floor #3
Q.C. Engr. Supvr. Product "A"
Q.C. Engr. Supvr. Product "B"
Q.C. Engr. Supvr. Product "C"
Inspectors Clerk
Inspectors Clerk
Inspectors Clerk
Inspectors Clerk
Inspectors Clerk
Inspectors Clerk
Supvr. C & M Lab
Supvr. Admin. & Statistics
INSPECTION LINE ORGANIZATION
Q. A. ENGINEERING STAFF

Fig. 3-4

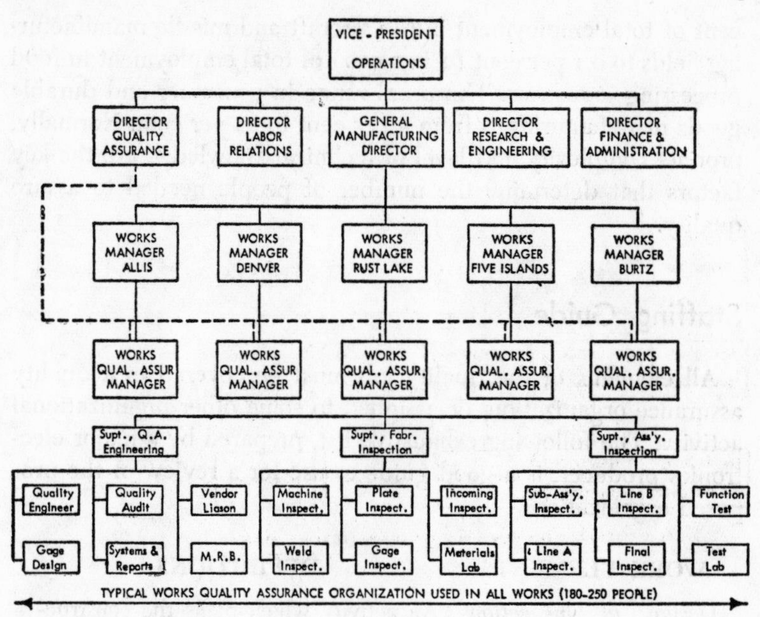

Fig. 3-5

Organization Errors

Frequently, quality assurance organizations are created which are excessively costly. Some of the symptoms are:

1. Excessive numbers of assistants.
2. One-over-one supervision.
3. Too few subordinates.
4. Excessive layers of supervision.
5. Grouping of unrelated functions under one supervisor.
6. Unreasonable staffing ratios.

Avoid this last condition and investigate what criteria competitors and similar noncompetitive industries use for quality staff size.

Quality assurance personnel may range from a high of 20 per

cent of total employment in the aircraft and missile manufacturing fields to 0.1 per cent (1 in 1,000) of total employment in food processing industries. The usual range in consumer and durable goods manufacturing is from 5 per cent to 12 per cent. Normally, product complexity and level of technical knowledge are the key factors that determine the number of people needed to assure quality.

Staffing Guide

All elements of the quality job must be covered in a quality assurance organization, or assigned to some other organizational activity. The following exhaustive list, prepared by a major electronics producer, is a good guide to use for a review of the proposed organization:

WORK ELEMENTS	DEFINITIONS
Design of inspection equipment	An activity which plans the construction of gages and fixtures to be used for measuring dimensional and visual characteristics of materials, parts, assemblies, and finished products.
Design of test equipment	An activity which plans the construction of apparatus to provide required inputs and measure resulting outputs of materials, parts, assemblies, and finished products.
Construction and/or procurement of inspection equipment	An activity which makes or procures gages and fixtures used to measure required dimensional and visual characteristics of materials, parts, assemblies, and finished products.
Construction and/or procurement of test equipment	An activity which makes or procures apparatus to provide required inputs and measure resulting outputs of materials, parts, assemblies, and finished products.
Calibration of inspection equipment	An activity which compares and adjusts or correlates dimensional and optical measuring devices to standards.

Calibration of test equipment	An activity which compares and adjusts or correlates input-output measuring devices to standards.
Maintenance of inspection equipment	An activity which keeps dimensional and optical measuring devices in working condition.
Maintenance of test equipment	An activity which keeps input-output measuring devices in working condition.
Training of inspectors	An activity which trains inspectors in the techniques of inspecting materials, parts, assemblies, and finished products.
Training of testers	An activity which trains testers in the techniques of testing materials, parts, assemblies, and finished products.
Inspection of incoming materials	An activity which verifies that materials, parts, and assemblies procured from outside the company for inclusion in the finished product meet required dimensional and visual characteristics.
Test of incoming materials	An activity which verifies that materials, parts, and assemblies procured from outside the company for inclusion in the finished product meet required input-output characteristics.
Inspection of work in process	An activity which verifies that parts and assemblies produced within the plant for inclusion in the finished product meet required dimensional and visual characteristics.
Test of work in process	An activity which verifies that parts and assemblies produced within the plant for inclusion in the finished product meet required input-output characteristics.
Inspection of finished products	An activity which verifies that finished products meet required dimensional and visual characteristics.

Test of finished products	An activity which verifies that finished products meet required input-output characteristics.
Special inspection and test	An activity which verifies, by means of visual, mechanical, chemical, physical, electrical, and other inspections and tests, that processing materials not included in the finished product meet specifications.
Disposition of discrepant material	An activity which decides whether to rework, screen, use as is, scrap, downgrade, or otherwise dispose of discrepant materials, parts, assemblies, and finished products.
Failed parts analysis	An activity which determines the kind and cause of failure of materials, parts, assemblies, and finished product.
Inspection of product packing	An activity which verifies products to be shipped to customers are identified, packed, loaded, braced, and routed as required.
Test of product	An activity which verifies, after engineering tests, that the specified containers and packing materials protect the product adequately against damage and deterioration.
Appraisal of quality of finished products	An activity which evaluates the finished products to determine how well the products being shipped meet customer requirements.
Establishment of quality standards	An activity which specifies, by means of documents and physical specimens, required appearance characteristics of materials, parts, assemblies, and finished products.
Writing quality assurance manuals	An activity which initiates and revises documents that describe the quality policies and quality operating procedures of the plant.
Inspection planning	An activity which determines the location of inspection points, the kind and amount of inspection to be performed,

	the procedures to be followed, the characteristics to be measured, the equipment to be used, the forms to be used, and the records to be kept.
Test planning	An activity which determines the location of test points, the kind and number of tests to be performed, the procedures to be followed, the characteristics to be measured, the equipment to be used, the forms to be used, and the records to be kept.
Maintenance of quality records	An activity which collects, sorts, summarizes, files, and maintains inspection and test data on materials, processes, parts, assemblies, and finished products.
Processing and reporting of quality data	An activity which plans and performs the analysis and synthesis of inspection and test data on materials, processes, parts, assemblies, and finished products.
Trouble shooting sporadic quality problems	An activity which investigates day-to-day quality problems, isolates the immediate causes, and recommends immediate corrective action.
Investigating chronic quality problems	An activity which investigates long-range quality problems, isolates the basic cause, and recommends permanent corrective action.
Follow-up of corrective action	An activity which monitors and reports progress in the implementation of solutions to quality problems and measures their effectiveness.
Appraisal of the quality assurance system	An activity which evaluates the quality assurance organization and procedures to determine their adequacy in meeting customer quality requirements at minimum cost.
Quality cost analysis	An activity which breaks down the plant's quality costs into meaningful classifications and points out areas of maximum potential reduction.

Vendor quality evaluation	An activity which works to evaluate the quality capabilities of a vendor from past performance and vendor facility reviews.
Contacts with vendors on quality problems	An activity which works with vendors in eliminating nonconformance to required characteristics of supplied materials, parts, and assemblies.
Tolerance review	An activity which reviews tolerance on the specified quality characteristic of materials, parts, assemblies, and finished products to determine whether they genuinely represent the limits of acceptability.
Quality review of customer requirements	An activity which compares written or implied customer requirements with the process and product capabilities of the plant.
Field failure analysis	An activity which determines and classifies the causes of failure of finished products which have been delivered to customers.
Quality review of product specifications	An activity which compares written or implied product specifications with customer requirements.
Customer contacts on quality problems	An activity which works with customers in eliminating nonconformance to required characteristics of finished products.

Implementing the Organization Plan

Two parallel but overlapping information systems are necessary within the quality assurance operation. One handles the product information, guiding corrective action and determining product acceptability and improvement. The second must provide the requisite information about the quality assurance department which the manager needs to operate efficiently.

How to Organize

Step one Obtain a clear statement of corporate objectives from top management. Top management must define the company's objectives; then the quality assurance manager must obtain a precise understanding of these objectives. He can then determine his department's requirements. He must also obtain a clear definition of the scope, responsibility, and authority within which he and his people are to operate.

Step two Prepare a statement of quality objectives as a means of coordinating departmental goals with those of the entire company. This source document, agreed on by top management, can be used as the key guidepost in organizing and managing quality assurance activities. Consequently, targets should be described quantitatively as well as qualitatively whenever possible.

For example, top management may have stated, as a corporate objective, that "where practical, lead time of purchased materials is to be reduced to six weeks or less to conserve operating capital." The quality assurance manager must then set up necessary objectives and systems to assist in meeting this requirement. He will need to further define and clarify the corporate objective in terms of quality assurance operations by stating that:

(a) Receiving inspection is to be completed and disposition made within two days following receipt of shipment;
(b) The system is to be so set up and controlled that the reliability of this problem is to be at least 95 per cent; and
(c) If at least 95 per cent of the monthly receipts are not cleared within the specified time, the quality assurance manager is to be notified and corrective measures taken.

Step three Draw up a departmental organization chart, reflecting the type of organization which will meet the departmental objectives on a continuous basis, and utilize the talents of available personnel with maximum effectiveness. This should be an extension of the corporate organization chart, defining the individual positions and showing the various levels and relationships between jobs. It should give a complete picture of the department structure and, as far as possible, insure that the formal and "informal" organization will be the same.

Step four Job descriptions are essential for the positions shown on the organization chart. These can be written in cooperation with the company's job evaluation or industrial relations staff. If they already exist, tactful re-education of the industrial relations staff is required to obtain needed changes. It is important to give each position the scope and responsibility that will enable the employee to contribute his share toward meeting Quality Assurance's objectives. The descriptions can then be used in job evaluation studies and in setting up an equitable salary structure. Without job descriptions and a sound basis of compensation, the department will be handicapped by dissatisfactions and misunderstandings.

Step five A policy and procedures manual should be compiled which defines the quality systems developed by the department and their relationship to other departments. It should establish specific procedures for the internal operation of the quality assurance function. This manual is a valuable training aid in integrating each person's job with the over-all goals of the company and the department, and in developing the individual employee. This aspect of the quality manual's usefulness is often overlooked.

Step six A manpower rating and inventory system should be introduced to provide for the continuous maintenance of the quality assurance organization as it was planned. It should show the quantity and quality of manpower available to fill any job in the quality assurance department, indicating the relative effectiveness of each man in his present job and the readiness of his replacement. Whatever system is used, the quality assurance manager should be able to see his needs at a glance and have a basis for planning his manpower development program.

Step seven After the job descriptions have been set up, establish the criteria to be considered in measuring not only individual performance, but departmental effectiveness as well. The job evaluations made in writing up the descriptions and determining the salary structure contain most of the standards needed to measure performance on each job. However, these may have to be expanded in some cases to add measures of quantitative performance. When measuring departmental effectiveness, factors should be evolved which relate to accuracy, service, costs, and other performance areas. What matters is the actual accomplishment, not how good a try was made.

Planning

Planning is a multiple role. It is the second basic step in the management cycle of any successful operation, including an efficient quality assurance department. One of its purposes is to relate the organization as originally laid out to actual operations. The quality assurance manager cannot effectively direct, control, appraise, and improve his operations, no matter how well his department is organized, unless he first plans his activities. To try to operate without continuous planning on a long- and short-term basis will lead to results far below the attainable optimum. Secondly, the operating plans put into motion the previously completed organizational structure designed to assure the attainment of corporate goals. Not only do operating plans and schedules provide guidance in daily operations, but they also serve as the basis for comparing results and establishing variances for review and control.

The planning function can be broken down into five integrated steps.

First step Each objective established for the quality assurance department should be converted into a statement of the general requirements needed to achieve it. For example, the goal of completing receiving inspection and making disposition of incoming material within two days following receipt of a shipment. This necessitates the establishment of tools and techniques that will guarantee adequate receiving inspection within the prescribed time limits. These requirements might include training or retraining programs for inspection personnel, an engineering analysis of the inspection area layout and equipment, review of clerical requirements, investigation of inspector efficiency by some such technique as work sampling, etc.

The statement should set up requirements for the long term from over one to five years into the future, as well as the current year by converting the specified planning requirements into effective functions, activities, projects and programs.

Second step Develop short- and long-term operating plans. Each specific requirement in the statement must be outlined in the operating plan needed to achieve it. Again, both a plan for the current year and one reaching five years into the future are desirable.

All these functions, activities, projects, and programs must be developed with respect to the scope, depth and approach needed to meet the short- and long-term requirements established. This information need not be written down in detail but should be outlined sufficiently to facilitate precise planning on an annual basis.

Third Step When the operating plans for each objective have been completed, estimate the required manpower on an annual and a long-term basis. (See Fig. 3-6.) This forecast should show the number of people needed in each job classification to meet the department's operating requirements during the current year, and the estimated long-range requirements. It should also show the job assignments—projected for each man—that are essential to handling all the functions, activities, projects and programs included in the operating plans. These projected assignments should fit into the job descriptions or the descriptions should be modified. Finally, the manpower plan should summarize the number of employees who will be working on each activity and, whenever possible, provide an estimate of the approximate time allocation.

Manpower planning is sometimes done in a cursory fashion, but it is often the key to the success of the operating program.

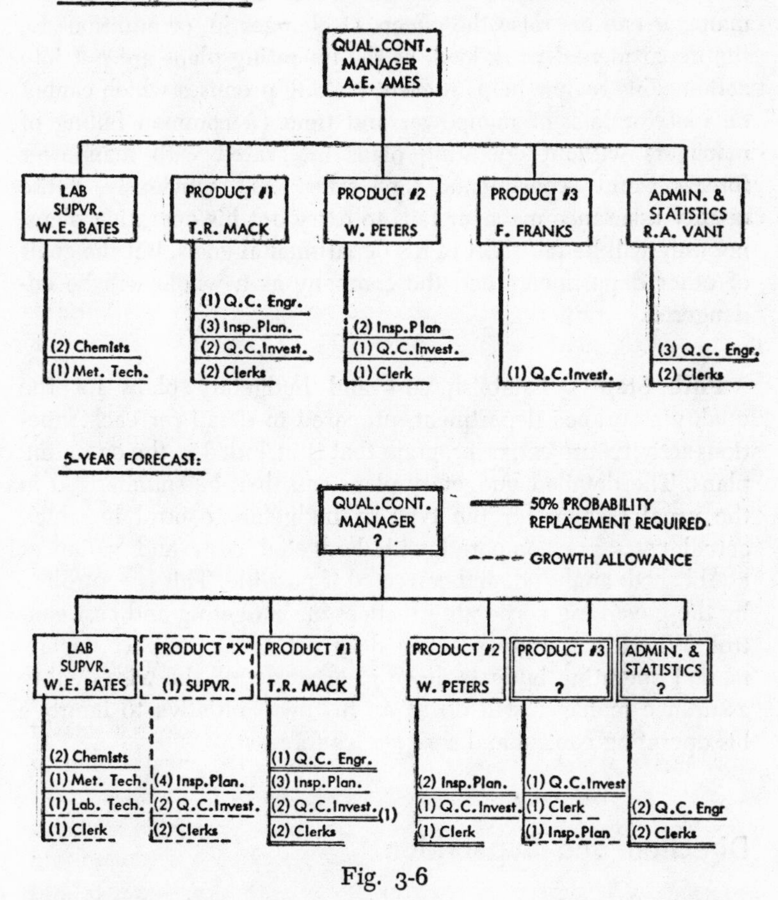

Fig. 3-6

The operating program should reflect corporate objectives precisely. It is imperative that the quality control manager forecast his requirements accurately to meet established goals on schedule.

Fourth Step A time schedule for the year should be developed on the basis of the manpower forecast. This schedule, by setting up appropriate targets, helps balance manpower availability against work load. At the same time, it enables quality assurance management to give priority to appropriate activities. The time schedule also serves as a basis for comparing actual progress with planned accomplishment. By reviewing it, the manager can appraise the effects of changes in, or additions to, the departmental work load, as the operating plans are put into action. This review helps prevent making promises which cannot be met for lack of manpower and time (a common failing of managers without operating plans integrated with manpower forecasts and departmental time schedules). Obviously, if the quality assurance manager fails to carry out his operating plans, not only will he fall short of his departmental goals, but the goals of other departments and the company as a whole will be endangered.

Fifth Step Establish cost and budgetary plans for the quality assurance department, prepared in detail for each function, activity, project, or program that is included in the operating plans. The detailed budgetary plans can then be summarized in the usual fashion for the type of budgetary control in which actual costs are compared with budgeted costs and variances established, analyzed, and corrected if possible. This is controlled by the governing corporate practices on budgeting and cost control. Where corporate practice does not break indirect departmental operating budgets down in great detail, the wise quality assurance manager will do so on his own initiative to improve his operating control and sharpen his forecast.

Direction and Supervision

Some of the basic elements that are essential to success in directing the activities of the quality control department are:

1. **Effective decision making.**
2. **Effective communication and delegation of authority.**
3. **Effective motivation and supervision.**
4. **Effective coordination and unification.**

Properly integrated, these four combine into a positive and progressive force to give the department the guidance necessary to the carrying out of the plan and programs.

As the planning phases in his operation proceed, the quality assurance manager should encourage various people to participate in making and developing proposals. But the resulting plans are the responsibility of the manager, who must review them and then accept, revise, postpone, or reject them. It is his responsibility to make the final decisions.

Controlling Results

Control of quality assurance department *operations,* as distinct from quality assurance of the product or service, will insure that department activities are carried out in accordance with the operating plans.

The basic steps in control are:

1. Measurement of progress and results.
2. Comparison of results with plans.

The important thing is to watch all significant indicators or measurable factors in performance. These should be measured for accuracy, quantity, and timing in quantitative terms whenever possible and reported in graph, chart, or report form. (See Fig. 3-7.) Because no system of measuring progress is of value unless results are compared with plans, variances must be established. Then list the variances as they occur to determine whether or not they are meaningful and action is required.

Control of operations is becoming increasingly more important. It is not enough to measure costs alone. Yardsticks must also be applied to all the elements of planned operations. Often standards can be set on the basis of historical operation, competitors' practices, or trade practices as published in various journals, until such time as valid standards can be built up in current operations. Trends as well as actual quality and quantity of job per-

QUALITY CONTROL
1961
Quality Costs
(% of Quality Costs to Direct Labor)

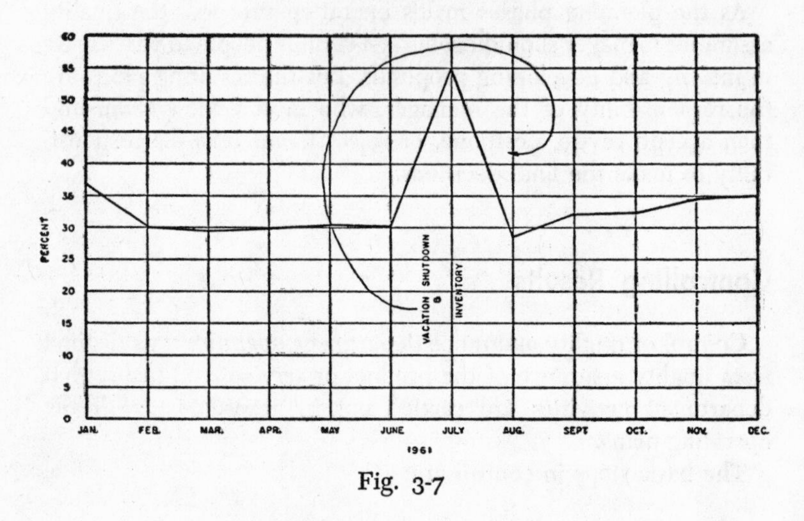

Fig. 3-7

formance can be compared. The control chart can be used by the quality assurance manager as well as by his people!

Performance Appraisal

Appraisal is primarily aimed at evaluating the results of operating plans on a continuous basis. In other words, the performance measured in the control phase of management is reviewed, then thoroughly analyzed to establish the cause of any deviation, so that the proper changes can be made in either plans or practices. Appraisal and control are very closely allied and are often considered to be part of the same management technique. However, there is considerable value in considering each separately to make sure the appraisal is actually undertaken. Often there is a tendency to issue control reports which measure results and variances but which never lead to appraisal and subsequent action. Thus the appraisal skill of the quality assurance manager is essential in pointing the way to correction and improvement within his own department.

The appraisal of results consists of the analysis of variances and performance evaluation. The purpose of variance analysis is to investigate the variances discovered during the control process. Whenever the outcome of any action differs significantly from what was planned, the need for correction is indicated. Thorough study of the variances will lead to the proper steps: correction of the original plan to reflect new conditions or information, correction of the course of action which leads to the variance, or a change in both the plan and the course of action.

Variance analysis works on the principle of management by exception in that management attention is directed primarily to trouble areas. If operating plans have been well worked out and the results are satisfactory, usually all that is required is intermittent reappraisal, rather than continuous appraisal of individual items.

The second element in appraisal is evaluation of performance factors contributing to the realization of the established plans. Some of these factors can be measured. Others need to be evaluated qualitatively. One of the tools for performance evaluation is the criteria set up while organizing the department. A second is the more detailed standards that result from planning. Various appraisal sheets, records, reports, charts, and graphs can be used to record and consolidate the needed information. In addition, an occasional management audit of over-all departmental results provides a comprehensive evaluation of performance.

Performance Improvement

In a properly managed quality assurance department, improvement is built into the daily activities. It is a continuous activity and without it optimum results are impossible.

Basically, improvement of operations involves:

1. Corrective action where indicated by unfavorable variances.
2. Preventive action to discourage unfavorable variances.
3. Modification of plans to better operations.

4. Development of short-term advances.
5. Research on long-term advances.

Corrective action Frequently, the greater part of the quality assurance manager's available time is devoted to corrective action which simply adjusts and changes past practices which have led to unfavorable variances. Corrective action improves operations, and is certainly essential, but the fact that it is necessary may mean that organizing, planning, and directing skills need review to assure they are being properly applied. "Putting out fires" or "crisis management" is a vicious cycle. When organizing, planning, and directing are weak, the manager spends most of his time coping with emergencies and correcting mistakes.

Preventive action Analysis will show the causes of unfavorable variances that need correction; but the quality assurance manager must take preventive action to avoid the recurrence of future variances in the same or similar circumstances. Preventive action may be initiated not only by variance analysis but also by performance evaluation. This occurs when evaluation detects unsatisfactory conditions or practices which should be corrected, but which have not yet resulted in unfavorable cost, quality, or time variances.

Plan flexibility Variances may occur because the plan is inadequate or improper; in fact, variance analysis or evaluation of results may indicate that plan modification rather than strict adherence will produce optimum performance. Therefore, it is essential that plans are flexible and permit occasional modification. Of course, modification often necessitates a series of changes, and care must be taken not to introduce some new factor or disturb some other sequence of steps and thus offset any gains. For example, the planned inspection of a new product may be modified to use automatic inspection equipment, provided the necessary change-over is not excessively costly in time or money and the new equipment does not require extensive "debugging."

Research improvements The quality assurance manager must also make *breakthrough* improvements that require development over a short or a long term. For example, the introduction of data-processing concepts in handling quality control data. This requires scheduled time and attention aside from the daily routine. Operations research has advanced quality control operations in several companies. The mathematical tools and techniques applied to researching the area of quality assurance management have led to major breakthroughs in operations improvement. Queuing theory, EVOP, simulation, and game theory are effective in the long-range improvement of quality control operations.

The Manager's Job

A quality assurance manager can divide his daily work into three logical categories. These are:

1. Management of his own staff.
2. Assurance of sound technical service, or inspection and quality control, for the operating organization.
3. Advice to management on quality control and related activities.

Staff The duties of his assistants must be planned and performed in a precise and orderly manner. The performance of the quality assurance organization should be a *quality* performance. Shoddily prepared procedures, letters, and reports, poor personal appearance on the part of staff members, bad housekeeping in the quality assurance offices and areas indicate the lack of a *quality* approach. Quality begins at home. Shortcomings here can undermine the effectiveness of quality assurance.

Technical adviser The quality assurance organization must maintain accurate, workable inspection standards and controls based on logical procedures and accurate data. In addition, it should provide assistance to line managers who seek advice on particular quality problems and advice to top management on quality assurance requirements.

Manager's Qualifications

The quality assurance manager should be acquainted with the broad aspects of the sciences and techniques of quality control, and have a capacity for generalization. The narrow specialist may possess one or even several of the post's qualifications, but to do a sound job of managing his people and of advising top and line management, he must have the stature, understanding, and maturity of a good manager. The unfortunate experiences of many firms prove ability in the techniques of statistical quality control is not enough for success in quality assurance management.

For example, will it occur to the specialist that he, as quality assurance manager, should be in close touch with the company controller during the development of the new standard cost program? After all, this covers direct labor and material, not quality assurance! However, will this new program cause manufacturing supervision to try to hide excess labor costs in scrap and rework accounts? Might a change in the costing practices increase the demand for earlier in-process inspection to minimize in-process inventory adjustment? And a dozen other questions that a good manager will bring to light? Who will raise such questions if the quality assurance manager does not? Should they not be discussed before the scrap and rework rate suddenly rises 55 per cent and the manager is on the carpet to explain the rise?

The successful administration of any quality control program depends on a manager with the following qualities:

1. **Knowledge of the business.** This includes a detailed knowledge of purchasing, sales, and production techniques, as well as of customers, personnel and labor relations, budgets and cost accounting, traffic and general management policy.

2. **Knowledge of the people in the firm.** The quality assurance manager often obtains his best results through the acceptance he has built for himself and his ideas in other divisions of the company. Evidence proves that quality assurance failure is

more often due to the manager's inability to cope with human problems than actual inspection or quality control failures.

3. **An orderly, rational mind.** The quality assurance executive is most likely to succeed if he has a mental capacity and emotional maturity which permit him to see people and situations in a clear and objective fashion, and recognizes not only his subordinates' but his own limitations in getting things done.

4. **A management attitude.** The most successful quality assurance men are primarily managers and secondarily quality control experts. They are professional in their approach to the job; they know its basic principles and they teach them to others. They are effective in interpersonal relations and are able to make diverse groups pull together to get results. They have an aggressiveness and drive which helps them to get things done. They normally make things happen rather than allow themselves to be shaped by circumstances. They identify with other managers rather than with specialists or technicians. They have a company rather than departmental attitude.

CHAPTER FOUR

Reliability and Quality

Reliability has only one meaning in the mind of the buyer of a product: *The product must work when he wants it to.* In more sophisticated technical language it means:

> *The purpose of a reliability program must be to design equipment to retain its initial status for as long a period as possible and to construct it in such a way as to make it easy to restore to the initial status when and if deterioration does occur.*[1]

The goal of reliability is product perfection; anything less is unacceptable because a mistake in quality or a failure of product reliability in just one product unit will mean a lost customer. The customer has every right to be unforgiving. The company took his money, didn't it?

Product service, however skillful, cheap, and prompt, is an inadequate substitute for product quality and reliability.

Warranty costs are one of the best indicators of the lack of product reliability. Scrap, repair and other internal costs are also

[1] Gordon H. Beckart, *1963 ASQC Annual Convention Transactions* (Milwaukee, Wisconsin, American Society for Quality Control), p. 126.

some measure of reliability; but to a great extent these factors also reflect a lack of quality control, and not necessarily life degradation which is more probably due to the design of the product. Progressive management, therefore, is increasingly aware that the measure of its reliability effort is success in reducing warranty costs and customer complaints.

There are several methods, other than warranty costs, used to determine the life of the product. Various tests which determine life characteristics, as well as reliability acceptance tests, usually reveal priorities for efforts aimed at resolving high-failure rate problems for military suppliers. Nonmilitary industry is not unfamiliar with the usefulness of life and failure-rate testing. But nonmilitary testing has been minimal, and much of it is statistically unsound. Still, the potential from testing in this manner is significant and inexpensive. In the appliance and automobile industries employees use the product to a great extent. This is an excellent source of well-controlled data.

In many organizations designs are developed by engineers in cooperation with sales and marketing personnel. When manufacturing finally sees the design it is close to or actually "frozen." Manufacturing is then directed to produce the product reliably, to a specific schedule, and for a specific price. The result is often confusion, recrimination, redesign of the product on the production line, delays, and loss of reliability. Early coordination of effort and reliability testing of product models should prevent most of these problems.

Management's Responsibility for Reliability

One of top management's basic functions is to decide the degree of reliability required in the product. Unfortunately, top management often passes the buck and never makes this decision. In many cases decisions on a required level of reliability are made by factory inspectors and production workers, with no marketing information to guide them.

Top management must also decide the extent to which the company will back up the product's performance financially and guidelines must be set up to cover guarantees, warranties, and policy adjustments on the use of the product. This decision leads to another regarding the type, nature, and extent of repair or service facilities for the product. For example, it is traditional for a company manufacturing typewriters to provide an extensive national service organization for after-sale maintenance of the product. This producer's basic policy is not to market a product until its service organization is trained to service it.

In other lines of business, the reduction in independent service facilities has forced companies to do some serious thinking on reliability. If the reader has tried to obtain a competent plumber lately, he knows what this means! In addition, the increasing warranty coverage in terms of length of time, and its use as a sales tool, has focused emphasis on product performance. The automobile industry is a good example of both of these trends.

One last point on service after sale: In the business machine industry and others, particularly with the rapid growth of leasing, most service is performed under a one-year, fixed price maintenance contract sold to the customer. It is not unusual for the sale of such contracts to amount to 10 per cent to 15 per cent of a company's gross sales volume. A change in the reliability of the product can have a marked effect on the ability of these service contracts to create profits or losses for the entire corporation. A 10 per cent change in service cost, either up or down, will affect the net profits of the company 25 per cent to 30 per cent, even though there is no change in warranty losses.

Function

The purpose of a general reliability program is to ensure that the device or product is designed to perform under anticipated conditions of environment, operation, and maintenance. For example, in the case of the electric typewriter, these conditions are subject to great variation throughout the world at various points of usage. Like other complex mechanical products, the basic reliability problem here is to establish from a limited number of models the design parameters and predict the probable success in meeting operating criteria for each machine of thousands produced, and if the probability is not satisfactory, to do something to improve it. This *getting something done* is the great omission in the minds of many people intimately concerned with reliability today.

A large number of these reliability practitioners are bemused with a numbers game they play. Predictions of reliability are made, consisting of a decimal point followed by a long string of nines. Then reliability allocations are made. That is, the decimal followed by a long series of nines for the whole product is divided into more decimals and strings of nines and allocated to various components of the product. Elaborate testing and reporting systems are then created to determine how closely the product approaches the predictions. This is good. It helps direct attention and effort to areas where work needs to be done. But *statistics and testing are not ends in themselves; they must be aimed at making the product work when the button is pushed.* Otherwise, as one operating missile manager sourly states, "A .99994 reliable manned space vehicle which fails on its first shot is merely one of the most expensive coffins in the world."

Some Definitions

Inherent reliability is the potential reliability of a product created in the design by the design engineers. It is the maximum reliability possible for that design and is seldom achieved in practice.

Achieved reliability is the reliability demonstrated in actual service by the manufactured product. It is less than design reliability and differs in each product unit due to the effects of manufacturing variability.

Environmental conditions are the applications, temperatures, humidities, and other operating conditions which the product will be exposed to in its service life. They include conditions encountered in packing, shipping, merchandising, and product service or repair. For example, today's kitchen utensils must be designed to withstand very hot water, due to the increasing use of domestic automatic dishwashers. Automobile manufacturers are forced to consider high levels of salt-water corrosion, due to use of snow-melting salting techniques on streets and highways.

Maintainability is the sum of the product features and characteristics which contribute to the rapidity, economy, ease, and accuracy with which the product can be kept in, or restored to, service in its operating environment. Simply put: How hard is it to fix it?

Supportability is the probability that maintenance action will restore the failed product to service during a specified or acceptable downtime. In simple terms, can it be fixed in time?

Mean time between failures (MTBF) is a basic measurement of the reliability of the product, in terms of the mean average elapsed time between observed failures, either in service or on test.

Failure rate follows from MTBF and is expressed, through statistical techniques, as the probability that a given product or component will fail in a given time period under certain environmental conditions.

The "Bathtub" Curve This is probably the best predictive pattern for reliability and warranty cost prediction available. It has been repeatedly shown that products usually possess a pattern of failures as indicated in Fig. 4-1.

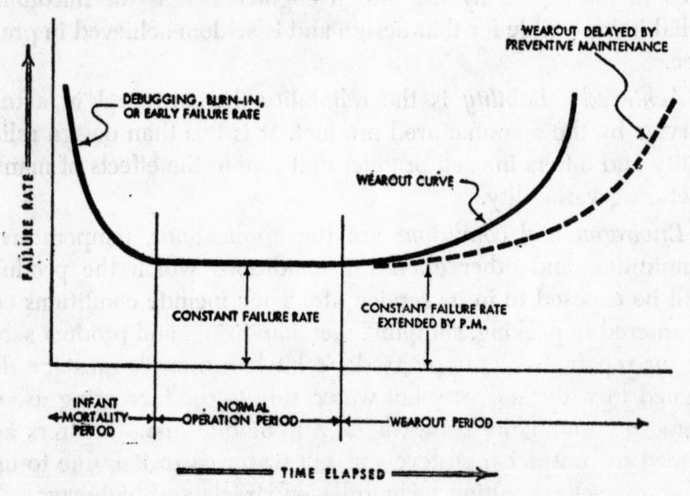

Fig. 4-1

Infant mortality is caused by the early failure of weak components or is due to operator misapplication, due primarily to nonrandom events or assignable causes. This creates an early high failure rate which falls off rapidly. Customer complaints may be high and service departments "debug" the new units. As repairs are made and bad components replaced, the failure rate drops.

Constant failure rate, or product "middle age," is due to random failures appearing at random intervals, but with a fairly constant average rate of failure for a given period of time.

Wearout occurs after long use. The failure rate rises rapidly and becomes so frequent there is no longer any useful life in the product. Wearout can be delayed by preventive maintenance which will prolong the period of the constant failure rate.

Procedures are available to determine these factors for any product statistically. These procedures fall beyond the scope of this book. Sources for reliability statistics are in Appendix A.

Role Conflict With Engineering

It should be obvious that a reliable product must be designed that way, that the engineer who originates its concepts is in the best position to make it reliable, and that it isn't properly designed until it is reliable.

However, most *reliability engineering* has used a statistical approach to evaluating test and field failure results. It has not been necessarily allied with Engineering and in many cases has overlapped into areas of Quality Assurance and Control. This has led to conflict within the organization.

As a result management is demanding a clarification of the reliability and quality assurance responsibilities and functions and elimination of duplication and friction between these areas where it exists.

The relationship of quality assurance and the reliability effort conflict because some believe that reliability is merely another aspect of the quality assurance function. Others feel that the function belongs to the engineering department. Still others believe that both should be equal units answering to an independent director of reliability and quality assurance who in turn reports to top management.

This organizational conflict does not really matter. The reliability responsibility is going to gravitate to Quality Assurance or Engineering or any other group that understands it, can perform its function, and is strong enough to seek it. Isn't it true in most organizations that over the years they have developed their own environment, different and distinct from that of other companies? No one "ideal organization" can fit all situations. To recommend predetermined organizational structures, based upon block diagrams with no relationship to the environment of a particular company, causes confusion and chaos.

The logical solution to any organizational structure is to determine how the existing natural lines of communication work. Determine who the natural leaders are, and where the lines of authority and responsibility have actually come to exist. Then, assure that the line of authority follows line of responsibility and actual performance for any function.

If you have a strong quality assurance function, sophisticated in quality control methods, technically capable in defect prevention techniques, and capable of learning and absorbing reliability theories and techniques, it will probably be the natural focus for your reliability function. On the other hand, a quality control organization which is merely an inspection force with little awareness of quality control techniques would not be qualified to organize a reliability function. Similarly, a strong and versatile engineering department may be the proper location for a new reliability operation.

Whether or not a quality assurance department has the organizational responsibility for reliability, it certainly must support the efforts. Therefore, it must have the basic understanding that elapsed time to failure data is recorded as a matter of habit. It must require failure reports at every stage of the manufacturing process and add this valuable data to the product's life history.

Reliability Controls and Problems

Regardless of who gets the job, the reliability engineering effort must include the following functions:

1. Develop, administer, and manage reliability programs for all products.

2. **Establish** standards for components.

3. **Approve** preparation of drawings and specifications for all parts, materials, and components; control subsequent changes.

4. **Estimate** numerical reliability ratings for subassemblies and products.

5. **Set up** reliability test programs to prove design and verify reliability ratings.

6. **Evaluate** prototypes for acceptable configuration.

7. **Monitor** design, conformance and performance.

8. **Establish** and maintain standards for calibration and maintenance of all measuring equipment, and control all test procedures.

9. **Review** and analyze all accumulated reliability data.

Reliability Check List

After responsibilities have been defined and categorized, check points are established where reliability decisions will be most useful. These include:

Proposal review.
Contract review.
Drawing review.
Design change approval.
Qualification and acceptance test specification review.
Design qualification tests.
Engineering prototype acceptance tests.
Design reliability demonstration tests.
Make-or-buy review.
Vendor/subcontractor selection.
Vendor acceptance test procedures.
Approval of vendors' quality and reliability organization.
Acceptance gaging approval.
Production tooling approval.
Measurement standards and instrument calibration.

Process certification.
Manufacturing environment.
Raw material inspection.
Material handling and stock control.
In-process inspection.
Manufactured and purchased component testing.
Assembly inspection.
Final product inspection.
Production qualification and acceptance tests.
Overhaul and repair inspection.
Preservation and packaging inspection.
Handbook verification.[2]

The check list above shows two major groupings:

1. Items closely associated with design and test engineering.
2. Areas chiefly serviced by quality control and inspection functions.

The second grouping will be discussed in Chapter Five. The first is discussed below.

Design and Test Engineering Functions

In many companies, designers have traditionally developed new designs in close cooperation with marketing. Quality assurance has usually been a manufacturing responsibility. But when manufacturing finally sees the new design, it is close to being "locked in." The usual result is confusion, dissension, recrimination, redesign on the production line, and customer dissatisfaction due to loss of reliability. Therefore, it is essential that the principle of *progressive design review* be applied to new designs and major revisions in older products.

Certain advocates of total quality control have implied that design should be organizationally and chronologically separated from the review activity. In this situation at review time review-

[2] Jack W. Curtis, "Reliability—A Management Tool," Quality Assurance, August, 1963, p. 23.

ers would descend on the designing engineers and bombard them with questions and criticisms. These reviewers, no matter how well intentioned, would certainly lack the necessary detailed background information the designers possess. Many of the reviewers' questions were resolved by the designers to their own satisfaction months before. Reviewers might also be concerned about concepts that should have been considered before the designers touched pencils to paper. No wonder designers are insulted and their management refuses to cooperate with such a review program.

Progressive design review This calls for continuing "give and take" conferences on a man-to-man or team basis between the design engineers and people with information about test results, field failure rates, and reliability statistics. Reviewers in this close and frequent contact with the designers acquire the extensive background information possessed by design people. Designers have a better opportunity to understand the reliability problems through close personal association with the reliability reviewers. The designer's habit of checking design logic in terms of *"Will it work?"* will be supplemented by the development of a reflex to check *"How will it fail?"*

Progressive review will also more easily detect critical situations and necessary design improvements, since any one review session is limited to the portions of the design added since the previous reliability review. Thus, maximum time is available for corrective action, project completion schedules are not imperiled, and the designer-reviewer relationship is not subjected to the strain of a finger-pointing contest as management determines who delayed the program.

The importance of the design reliability review function cannot be overstated. Managements familiar with reliability problems have learned that field failure follows the following pattern:

Responsibility for Failure	Percentage Amount of Total Problems
Engineering design	40%
Misapplication, service abuse	30%
Manufacturing quality	20%
Unclassified miscellaneous	10%

The prime area for reliability improvement is engineering design, and analysis will usually confirm that design improvements prevent field abuse and reduce manufacturing problems.

Policy Guides Prevent Review Conflicts There is no point in being naïve about the possibility of a large amount of conflict arising from the review program. It most definitely will! Therefore, it is essential that policies be set up, prior to the time of struggle, that clearly state how such situations are to be handled. Policies should specify when the recommendations of the reliability reviewers are to be enforced, and when the designer's opinion is to govern.

Years of quality control experience indicate the best approach is to establish and distribute written reliability standards. The reliability activity can then enforce these standards with the same authority to reject designs that do not conform as inspectors have to reject hardware not up to blueprint standards. Designs violating a reliability standard will be rejected and corrected, but when reliability has opinions about design deficiencies, but cannot show standards being violated, the designer's judgment will be law. In the few remaining grey areas, top management can be the final arbiter.

When such standards exist, they can be recast as check-off lists to be used by the designer in conception and the reliability reviewer in evaluation of the product design. No lengthy reports are required, and great savings of time are realized.

In attacking reliability problems, it is necessary to consider basic causes.

First Any product entity is always subject to change and is changing, although the rate of change or time scale may vary tremendously from one product unit to another. These changes are due to exposure to environment, to internal stresses and forces of operation, and abuse. Some of these factors are random, others nonrandom. Some cancel, some amplify, and most influence others on a random basis.

Second Reliability is usually arbitrary in defining its state of being. If a motor-driven valve will not close against a line pressure of 25 p.s.i., and in service it must do so, it is not reliable.

The fact it once closed under such line pressures, and still will close against a 24 p.s.i. line pressure, has no bearing on its reliability in that product at this latest point in time. Definition thus becomes a major problem. What is reliable performance?

Third Variability of characteristics which determine reliability are not the result of purely casual relationships. As a result of the many possible causes for a given effect and the unpredictability of these causes, the problem must be approached through the use of probability. Consider that if the reliability of an individual part is 99.990 per cent and 10,000 such parts (not an unreasonable number for a complex product) are used, the system reliability is only 37 per cent. To raise the reliability of such a system to 90 per cent it would be necessary to raise individual part reliability to 99.999 per cent. Also, with 99.990 per cent reliability, a product having 100 hours average failure-free operation requires parts that fail on an average of only once in 120 years. Remember, too, that in the first hour of operation there is a probability, no matter how slight, that a part may fail and sooner or later a product unit will be produced in which this happens!

How can this problem be solved?

The description of the problem above indicates three lines of approach:

1. Each unit, part, and subassembly can be made as stable and resistant to environment as is possible and necessary, and/or it can be protected from the environment.
2. Each unit, part, and subassembly can be made as simple as possible, using an absolute minimum of machined surfaces, soldered joints, components, etc.
3. Apply the theory of redundancy. That is, provide duplicate units in parallel with a given unit, so that if one unit fails another unit still performs the assigned function.

Reliability Applications

Resistance to environment and operational stability begin with the smallest unit, the component part. Strength of materials involved is usually well established, and there is normally a reasonably broad range of materials to choose from for a given application. It is usually possible to design mechanical parts so that they will withstand the expected environment with a suitable safety margin. Reliability problems in these two areas usually arise from errors in determining the environmental conditions. On the other hand, electrical components are often much more complicated than simple mechanical parts. They must possess a variety of electrical properties as well as being subject to mechanical limitations in their own right. Frequently, the required electrical and mechanical properties conflict with each other and it is seldom possible to obtain a satisfactory compromise between them. Finally, parts standardization, particularly in the field of electrical components, has further restricted the designer's design freedom. The design of standard parts by the very nature of the standardization process will always lag behind design demands.

There are only three courses of action that can be taken in developing reliable component parts:

1. **Determine,** through comparison testing, which is the best available part.
2. **Establish** through testing procedures that a particular part is satisfactory.
3. **Develop** a part that is satisfactory as determined by adequate tests.

The problem with methods 2 and 3 is that it is not always possible to clearly define what satisfactory performance is for a particular component. The desired reliability and environment for a finished product may be very well known. However, it is not easy to predict for a specific part within the product what its environment will be. Thus, although power lawnmowers normally operate at ambient temperatures between 45°F. and 110°F., they may well be stored in subzero temperatures and components near the engine or exhaust manifold may be exposed to temperatures upward of 750°.

Further, the requisite testing may be quite expensive and consume enormous amounts of time, involving the testing of thousands of units under varying environmental conditions for thousands of hours. Where standardized components are available, then, method 1 is most frequently adopted. One thing even the most enthusiastic advocate of reliability must consider is that the product must be marketed on a timely basis. It avails nothing if the company finally brings out the finest and most reliable buggy whip ever conceived ten years after the last buggy is sold.

Once suitable components are selected, consideration must be given to assembling and packaging the complete system or product. Ease of assembly and adjustment must be considered, as well as future demands for maintenance access and trouble shooting. Final packaging must minimize the deleterious effects of environment. This involves combating the effect of temperature extremes, contaminants, sealing, and shock and vibration. Also, some thought must be devoted to damage control, so that in the event of component failure, other units are not taken out of service by fire, blast, or other by-products of the initial failure.

Considering the total product or system, choose the simple solution in preference to the sophisticated one. All other elements being equal, tried and proved simple solutions are the best, being easiest and most familiar for both manufacturing and field service to cope with. If added complexity will give a longer service-free life and decrease maintenance costs overall, it is worth considering. Adequate testing should be performed to insure that this is the case.

Preventive maintenance programs enter into design concern at this point, since programed detection of incipient failures and the replacement of these deteriorating components before they quit will greatly improve total product reliability. Before placing too much reliance on this factor, however, the value of such a program must be thoroughly verified.

Redundancies This is one of the most powerful and useful solutions to the problem of reliability. Redundancy can be grouped into two types, known as series and parallel, and following the same theory used in electrical engineering to set up this nomenclature.

In series redundancy, successful equipment operation requires that a series of units function as a whole even though certain units do not operate. An example is the use of two derated amplification stages in an electronic circuit where one stage would suffice. This might be done to permit improvement of individual stage reliability. It is obvious that series redundancy is difficult if not impossible to apply to mechanical systems, and not often feasible or advisable in electrical application. In any case, the over-all gain in reliability is slight.

In parallel redundancy, successful system operation can occur when only one of several similar units functions properly. Parallel redundancy can be simple or sophisticated, and can be applied to mechanical or electrical systems. An excellent example is the human body, with the ability of its circulatory system to function with main pathways blocked. Its engineering application can give major increases in product reliability, but the cost, both in dollars and performance, may be high. Also, care should be taken that the "decision" device which decides which redundant component is to be used or bypassed does not in itself unduly complicate the system. If possible, continuous redundancy is preferable, so that no decision is required. Such redundancy exists in aircraft with duplicate hydraulic control boost systems continuously in operation, for example, or in electrical circuits that use capacitances in parallel to prevent short-circuit failures in blocking applications.

Life Testing From a practical point of view, the solution of a reliability problem is usually verified by life testing. This applies not only to the total product, but also to vendor designed and produced components incorporated therein. The most common life test program is 1,000 hours, and its results establish a failure rate in terms of per cent of units failing per thousand hours. Unfortunately, failure rates are not constant over extended periods of time. The largest percentage of failures is observed in an initial time interval with a diminishing effect as time goes by, followed by a rapid wear-out rate. This was discussed previously in the analysis of the bathtub curve of failure rates. Thus, the failure rate may be different for each thousand-hour period, and there is no way to tell accurately what part of the failure rate curve a thousand-hour life test covered.

Also, in the case of standard parts, different manufacturers of the same component may use different processes subject to different types and degrees of variability. This will cause failure modes and rates to vary. Capacitors from one manufacturer may fail by shorting out, while those of another manufacturer fail through open circuits in the leads. Each type of failure may cause radically different failures in the product involved. In addition, different modes of failure may appear under different applications at varying levels of load and stress. A device may be extremely reliable in continuous operation, but fail rapidly when cycled off and on.

Caution must be exercised in accepting derating of components as an indication of an extension of reliable life. Too often, there is no retesting program to adequately verify that derating has actually extended life as advertised. This is true when evaluating the results of accelerated testing programs. Is the data truly comparable to real operating conditions?

Operators and Equipment The reliability of the test equipment and test operators become major factors, particularly in testing components with very low failure rates. Other difficulties are experienced in testing components with high power input or output requirements, or units with extremely slow or lengthy cycles. Care must also be taken in standardizing test conditions before running comparative tests. This is particularly true when comparing test results from different vendors.

Verification of reliability in production is difficult and accompanied by old and new problems. Calibration of gages and test equipment is an old problem that has always concerned inspection and quality control departments. It is doubly important in a reliability program, where gage or tester drift can be mistaken for operating time deterioration of the product. Flinching by test operators also upsets test accuracy. Reviewing test readings usually shows few readings just at specifications limits. Instead, most observations are well away, on one side or the other, from the specification limit value. This can be offset, in part, through reliance on running time meters and recording instruments to overcome the human element.

Screening The search for reliability assurance has led many organizations to screening as a major control. In fact, some have overdone it to the point that it has adversely affected product reliability by testing or screening it to death. Excessive reliance on screening or, more bluntly, 100 per cent inspection, is costly and subject to all the hazards of any 100 per cent inspection operation. In short, it does not work. The answer, again, is to design and process for reliability under logical and effective management controls.

Screening also does not reflect the vital time element. In one case, molded plastic parts were well within specification limits when delivered and screened. After storage and measurements at periodic intervals, it was established that the parts shrank as they aged, and testing quickly demonstrated that this shrinkage caused failures. In this particular application, a change of material eliminated the problem.

"Run-in" and "Burn-in" Testing procedures widely used to fight infant mortality on a production basis are referred to as "run-in" for mechanical products and "burn-in" for electronic gear. A television set manufacturer uses a "hot-line" overhead conveyor system. TV receivers are connected to the line and allowed to run for about twenty-four hours. This short "burn-in" breaks down any weak components that could cause early failures. This manufacturer's quality planning has been so successful that initial failures are practically nil and use of the "hot-line" may soon be abandoned.

A manufacturer of business machines lays great stress on continuing reliability testing in production using automated test robots. This 100 per cent two-hour run-in test was based on a thorough analysis of a long program of testing new electric typewriters for periods of eight to forty hours. It was discovered in these longer tests that 81 per cent of the failures, malfunctions, and defects occurred in the first two hours of operation, 6 per cent in the final ten minutes of the test, and the remaining 13 per cent in the balance of the test, a period of six to thirty-eight hours. Management assumed that the 6 per cent found in the last ten minutes were the result of the test operator's final look at the machine prior to ending the test. This proved to be so. It was forecast, and later verified, that a two-hour test would find 87 per cent of the problems.

In reliability testing, as in any other industrial activity, you get what you pay for. Careful planning, particularly in minimizing influence by human or other extraneous factors, is required to make it pay off. But it will pay off. Cases are on record where change-overs to automated test equipment permitted greatly increased testing at reduced rates. In one instance involving small electrical motors, the test equipment paid for itself in eight months, and permitted a 600 per cent increase in testing time per motor.

CHAPTER FIVE

Functions

A quality assurance program covers six basic functional areas. These are:

1. Preproduction quality engineering.
2. Vendor quality relationships.
3. Incoming material quality assurance.
4. Process quality control.
5. Assembly quality control.
6. Quality verification and audit.

Each basic area checks the work of at least one other activity, and in turn is checked by one or more areas. This check and balance is a principal reason for this division of effort, and should be carefully observed in firming up the quality assurance organization discussed in Chapter Three.

Preproduction Quality Engineering

This activity embraces all items required to prepare for quality assurance from initial conception of a product, service, or company through production start-up. It includes the basic quality measures taken to cover all operations, and the specific actions taken on quality plans and requirements for a particular product. These functions, based on definitions established by the American Society for Quality Control,[1] are:

"Preparation and maintenance of a quality assurance manual, or other compilation of the methods and procedures to be used in quality assurance operations and company-wide quality controls. There is no necessity that this be a separate manual if corporate policies provide for a single or combined procedures manual for the company, as long as quality assurance personnel review the procedures for adequacy. Instructions, methods, and suitable forms are needed to control collecting, analyzing, and reporting quality and reliability data, disposition of discrepant material including allocation of responsibility and cost, corrective action, basic inspection procedures, and product review techniques and relationships. (See Fig. 5-1.)

"Determination and implementation of inspection and test facilities required for quality assurance and reliability operations. Again, the details of design and construction of the facilities may be done by others, but quality assurance personnel should determine both the original requirements and the degree to which these requirements are met by the proposed solutions and the delivered hardware. Include provisions for periodic and economical checks of precision and accuracy of all gages, fixtures, testing machines, measurement devices, and other physical and analytical facilities used to assure quality.

"Provide complementary human facilities for the quality assurance program through training programs for all levels of the organization, both within and without the quality assurance activity. Training should cover the entire range of quality assurance operations from basic shop mathematics for inspectors to advanced statistics for engineers. Strong consideration should be given to courses in product and process familiarization and customer product usage and operation. Again, look outside the immediate organization for assistance in this area. Local schools and

[1] *The Basic Work Elements of Quality Control Engineering* (Milwaukee, Wisconsin, American Society for Quality Control).

QUALITY PROCEDURES C-D ENGINE DIVISION	Q. P. No. 10-3 Date Rel. 12/3/XX Sheet 1 of 8 Sheets Effective Upon release Supersedes Orig. Issue

TITLE: Inspection Check Sheets.

PURPOSE: To specify the procedure for preparing, distributing, and revising Check Sheets - Purchased Parts Inspection (Form CDE-4103) and Check Sheet - Manufactured Parts Inspection (Form CDE-4104).

1. Responsibilities:

1.1. Quality Analysis.

1.1.1. Obtain pertinent data and classify quality characteristics of Purchased Parts and Manufactured Parts.

1.1.2. Prepare, distribute, and revise Check Sheets.

1.1.3. Maintain a master file of all marked blueprints and associated data, multilith mats, and Check Sheets.

1.2. Gage Engineering.

1.2.1. Specify the type of equipment required for inspection of characteristics of Purchased Parts.

1.2.2. Specify the gage number of equipment required for inspection of characteristics of Manufactured Parts.

1.3. Engineering.

1.3.1. Assist Quality Analysis in acquiring information required for classification of characteristics.

1.4. Manufactured Parts Inspection.

1.4.1. Maintain a file of Check Sheets - Manufactured

	APPROVAL	DATE		APPROVAL	DATE
Mgr. Qual. Cont.			Mgr. Prod. Engr.		
Gage Engr.			Mgr. D.P. & SYS.		
Pur. Parts Insp.			Mgr. Prod. Cont.		
Mfg. Parts Insp.					
Quality Analysis					
Quality Engr.			Genl. Mfg. Mgr.		

Fig. 5-1

colleges may offer exactly what is wanted, or be willing to modify their curriculum to meet a company's needs. Professional societies, trade and manufacturers' associations, and even the YMCA may have programs that fit industrial needs. There are also the various retraining programs sponsored by the Federal Government and administered by the several states which can be used for such purposes as training inexperienced new inspectors in basic skills.

"Establish quality standards for products, processes, and procedures as needed in the company. Modify standards as required due to in-plant and customer requirements feedback and advances in technology or the 'state of the art.' Take care, however, not to infringe in the legitimate areas of either engineering or the systems and procedures group for two reasons: One is to reduce conflict, of course, while the other is to insure that these people do not evade their own responsibilities.

"**Conduct product and process research through experiments and tests** designed to increase knowledge of variables affecting product and process quality and reliability. This should include evaluation of competitive products and other similar but noncompetitive product lines, and continuous search among newer production processes and techniques.

"**Analyze manufacturing, customer, and vendor problems** on prior designs and recommend engineering practices and specifications that are intended to eliminate such problems from new designs.

"**Use statistical methods to predict over-all tolerances of proposed designs** based on previous process capability studies. Submit to design engineering tolerance recommendations which enable desired over-all tolerances to be met and at the same time allow individual dimension tolerances to be within proved process capabilities.

"**Recommend to production engineering process improvements,** including fixtures, tools, jigs, production checks, and testing devices required to achieve process control and maintain desired quality and reliability.

"**Analyze tolerances, specifications, dimensions, and reliability characteristics** of product designs to assure that the product as manufactured will perform as required. Make recommendations for design changes required to reduce or eliminate problems.

"**In conjunction with incoming material quality assurance, plan tests, inspections, and statistical studies** on initial product or component samples. Analyze results to verify design's quality and reliability requirements. (See Fig. 5-2.)

"**Determine parameters of trial or pilot production lots to be measured and controlled** by process and assembly quality assurance. Analyze results. Predict the performance of future production lots. Prepare reports of trial data for design and production engineering and permanent record.

INCOMING INSPECTION DETAIL CARD

COMPONENT:	TYPES	W DWG., CAT. NO. OR MIL SPEC.
INSPECTION TYPE	1.	
(X)...ACCEPTANCE SAMPLING	2.	
	3.	
(A) INSPECT COMPLETE LOT	4.	
(S) SPOT CHECK 3PCS/LOT	5.	
	6.	
DEFECT CLASSIFICATION	7.	
(A) MAJOR (B) MINOR	8.	
	9.	
MINOR EQUAL MAJOR	10.	
	11.	
AQL:	12.	
REVISION NO. APPROVED	13.	
WRITTEN BY: ________	14.	
DATE	15.	

REMARKS: APPROVED BY:________ DATE____
Reviewed by Foreman Inc. Insp.
Matls.&Stds.:________ DATE____

CHARACTERISTICS TO BE CHECKED	MEASURING METHOD & EQUIPMENT	INSP. TYPE	DEFECT. CLASS
MECHANICAL:			
ELECTRICAL:			

NOTES:

SHEET___OF___SHEETS

Fig. 5-2

"**Make recommendations and/or establish procedures** for use in setting up economical methods of measuring and controlling production quality and reliability.

"**Assist in applying statistical and other quality control techniques and principles** to other management functions, such as operations research, safety, experimental work, finance, and other functions.

"**Develop new techniques and approaches for dealing with quality problems.** Cooperate with professional societies and other groups outside the company to advance quality assurance, including presentation of technical papers and publication of advances within the company to the profession."

The foregoing functions are intended to insure good preplanning of quality assurance operations, provide feedback to engineering to influence new products or obtain major revisions in older products, and provide a continuing drive for improvement in all quality assurance operations, including its own.

Vendor Quality

Vendor quality relationships are separated from incoming inspection in this discussion for two reasons. First, vendor relationships are basically a staff service to purchasing, engineering, and incoming inspection, and it is not wise to combine staff and line responsibilities in one function unless a truly broad-guage individual heads it up. Second, the conflict of interest problem is partially controlled by providing two separate activities to check vendor quality. Quality Assurance should:

Evaluate vendor quality performance capability and develop criteria for quality performance rating to aid Purchasing in selection and development of material sources. Many manufacturers make a practice of visiting vendor plants to check on methods and equipment to make sure they meet and maintain quality standards. (See Fig. 5-3.)

Provide vendors, through Purchasing-approved channels, with clear, concise quality and reliability requirements in writing. Follow up to insure adequate understanding and vendor action to meet these requirements.

Tell vendors how Quality Assurance will inspect their material to verify compliance with quality and reliability requirements. If checking fixtures are used, the vendor should be given

				VENDOR CHECK LIST #____ TITLE ____	
No	CHARACTERISTIC	A	U	N	COMMENT	RECOMMENDATION
9	Material is marked for production status					
10	Material is marked for inspection status					
11	Quality Assurance or Quality Control activity specifies inspection and test points.					
12	Adequate methods are used to identify and isolate defective material.					
13	Test and inspection records are available for review.					
14	Corrective action is planned and followed for completion.					
SURVEY BY:					P.O./CONTRACT: VENDOR:	

Fig. 5-3

either a duplicate fixture or the design drawings thereof with instructions from Purchasing to build his own duplicate fixture.

Coordinate approval of initial samples supplied by vendor and inspected by incoming material quality assurance with Purchasing and Engineering, if required. In general, a vendor should not be paid for tooling costs or start-up expenditures, nor for the initial sample shipment, until the sample is approved.

Insure that a suitable change control system exists to advise the vendor of changes in design requirements, and is used to inform vendors of changes in quality and reliability requirements. Inform the vendor of field failures in his product and help him through Purchasing to evolve corrective measures.

Work with suppliers to establish quality certification plans based on adequate procedures and controls at the suppliers' plants to minimize the cost of incoming material quality assurance. The objective is to shift the burden of proof of incoming quality to the vendor and put incoming material quality assurance out of business. This activity may include educating the supplier in quality assurance techniques.

Cooperate with Purchasing and/or other activities in value analysis, cost reduction, and other programs designed to reduce material and product costs. Quality costs are often ignored and this cooperation may help the vendor to justify costs incurred in this vital area.

Establish and monitor systems for recording and reporting supplier conformance to quality and reliability requirements. Establish a vendor quality rating system to guide Purchasing in selecting and retaining vendors. This rating system is not to be used as a crutch to shift the blame for failure to get corrective action on vendor quality problems entirely to Purchasing. Regardless of what the vendor rating says, as long as the vendor supplies the company, Quality Assurance shares with Purchasing the responsibility for getting problems corrected.

In reviewing vendor quality relationships, certain basic fundamentals must be kept in mind. It is unrealistic to try to get quality materials from inadequate sources. Quality Assurance has a large stake in improving the vendor selection process and insuring that it embraces quality as well as cost and schedule considerations. The vendor cannot be held to undefined requirements, but specified requirements which are not enforced are meaningless marks on a piece of paper. Finally, the company-vendor relationship is a legal one, under a written contract called the purchase order and, in extreme cases, subject to judicial review. Poor relations or unreasonable demands on suppliers injures the company's reputation as badly as product failure does.

Conflicts of Interest

A company must develop and maintain a reputation that warrants public confidence. Its employees must not be involved in, or even appear to be involved in, conflicts of interest. The principal area in quality assurance where such a situation can arise is in the vendor quality relationship function. By definition, a conflict of interest exists where an employee has a private financial interest or other relationship outside the company that could damage the interests of the company, even if it does not result in actual financial loss to the company, regardless of the employee's motives in establishing the relationship. Such situations in the quality assurance area might include:

1. *Any ownership interest by the employee, his family, or intimate acquaintances in a vendor.*
2. *The acceptance of gifts, entertainment, or other favors of more than a token nature that might place an individual under an obligation to someone with whom the company does business.*
3. *The use of one's position or knowledge in a way that might result in personal gain.*

Let's face it. A vendor does not present gifts or favors because he is enamored with one's big blue eyes. Sooner or later he will present a bill, in the form of a demand for acceptance of substandard material, improvement in an unsatisfactory rating, or other "nonfinancial" favors.

Measures to combat such situations include: rotation of personnel in vendor contact and incoming inspection areas to prevent build-up of close relationships with vendor people; regular reviews and audits of procedures and operations involving vendor contact; a well-publicized policy on acceptances of gifts, business lunches, etc.; and firm policing of this policy. Naturally this policy applies to the quality assurance manager as well as his people.

Incoming Material Inspection

This function enforces the requirements on the vendor through usual inspection practices. It is the line inspection counterpart of the vendor quality relationships function. It is also concerned with the handling and storage of purchased materials and components so that they do not deteriorate prior to use. This complete concept is vital because, if substandard material enters the production process, the burden of inspecting quality into the completed product becomes greater. A well-planned and properly executed program of incoming material quality assurance includes:

Development, installation, and maintenance of inspection and analytical procedures including economical sampling plans for determining quality levels of incoming materials.

Plans, procedures, and facilities for handling discrepant material. These must be realistic. Most purchased items are on short inventory levels and lead times to minimize company investment therein. The result?

1. When material is rejected on receipt for "minor" faults, some people may be tempted to expedite the rejected material into process without observing the formality of notifying incoming inspection. In brief, it is stolen.
2. Incoming inspection is frequently requested to screen defectives or arrange for in-plant rework, in preference to returning the material to the vendor. Incoming inspection operations must recognize these pressures and be prepared to thwart the first and accommodate the second.

Efficient operation, timewise, of incoming material quality assurance is a must. Incoming inspection cannot cause production delays due to its inability to get the stuff checked or to reach a decision.

Sufficient information concerning inspection and test results so corrective action can be initiated, vendor rating programs maintained, and future procurement decisions be placed on a factual basis as far as quality is concerned.

Economical statistical sampling procedures to appraise inventory quality, determine deterioration rates, and provide feedback to design, purchasing, and production which will aid in maximizing inventory serviceable life.

Certain measures of efficiency apply to incoming material quality assurance. These include:

1. The per cent of incoming lots rejected.
2. Distribution of rejected lots, whether reworked, sorted, returned to vendor, scrapped, or *used as is*. If *used as is* dispositions rise, watch out! Either incoming inspection is too tight or the product quality is about to deteriorate.
3. Length of time to process an average lot through incoming inspection.
4. Lots inspected per inspector per day, or other measure of time.
5. Size of backlog of uninspected lots.
6. Size of backlog of rejected lots awaiting disposition, and average time per lot for disposition decision to be made and effected.

Be sure your definition of incoming material is broad enough to assure product quality. What about drawings made by outside design services, plastic pellets, plating chemicals and solutions, masking tape, etc.? It is not always necessary to provide incoming quality assurance on every item, but every item must be thoughtfully reviewed to determine if such assurance is required or can be omitted. *Omit incoming inspection by plan, not by accident!*

Process Quality Control

Process quality control functions will vary widely due to variations in plant size, product mix, and processes employed. Effective process control has two major hurdles to leap.

1. It must not relieve manufacturing supervision of its responsibility for producing a quality product. At the same time it must assure only satisfactory material is released from the process.
2. It must provide this assurance at acceptable and reasonable costs. Any fool can set up an inspection plan that checks every part after every operation and bankrupt the company. Real skill is required to select and install manufacturing controls where they will do the most good at the least cost.

The majority of employees want to do a good job, take pride in their work, and in their company. If workers are trained to know right from wrong, and have the means to check their work, they will perform at the level of quality workmanship expected of them. Unfortunately, it is not uncommon in plants whose management complains about the death of craftsman instincts to discover that workers have absolutely no way to find out if parts produced are good or bad at the time they produce them. How can they act like craftsmen in such circumstances?

This natural desire for pride in work, properly channeled, is the cornerstone of process control and quality assurance. If production workers and their supervision know how to determine if the product and process are right or wrong, and have means for making such a determination, they can perform at the level of quality workmanship expected of them. Then true process control can be economically applied to assure that the manufacturing processes are performing as planned.

An effective process control system is built on four fundamentals:

1. **It is a planned activity.** All operations in the manufacturing processes are covered by detailed process control planning. These detailed plans must be developed by a technically qualified person, intimately familiar with the processes and the product involved. These process control plans or inspection instructions parallel the production process plan, routing sheet, traveler, or other information which instructs production in how to produce the parts. Instructions should include the list of characteristics to be checked at each operation; the manner of checking them;

time and frequency of checking; and identification of personnel to perform the check. Reference should be made to any quality standards, sampling plans, and acceptance levels to be applied, if they are not incorporated in the inspection instruction sheet itself. Reference should be made to the blueprint to be used, with some means of identifying the current applicable change or revision of that print.

2. **The plans must be easy to follow.** They must be simple, explicit, and easily understood. The most sophisticated plan conceived by a college-trained engineer is absolutely useless unless expressed in simple and clearly understood "shop talk." Not only the language or nomenclature should be simplified, but if data is to be recorded, as much as possible should be in the "check here" form. Printed forms should be clear, easily read, without fine print, and on sufficiently heavy stock to withstand the onslaught of greasy fingers. When measurements are required which cannot be put on a "go, no-go" basis, the simplest equipment with the most foolproof manner of use and reading should be specified.

3. **Tell everyone about the process control plans.** How often have you heard an operator say, "Nobody told me," or "I didn't know I was supposed to do that!" Familiarize everybody concerned with all details of the process control operation, and then go back and tell them again, and again, and again. Have a very broad definition of "everybody concerned." Tell the material handlers, the stockroom helpers, even the sweepers! Don't laugh! What do your sweepers do with the parts they find on the floors when they sweep?

Every operator, inspector, and supervisor must know what to look for, how to check it, with what, how to record his findings, and what action to take as a result. The written process control plans or inspection instructions should be communicated to operators and production supervision as well as to inspectors, by posting at the job with the parts prints and specifications.

4. **Assure that manufacturing operations comply with the process control plans.** Manufacturing processes must be monitored to assure operator familiarity with process control requirements; availability of required gages, which are both accurate and in use; that required records are on the job and kept current; and that the product produced conforms to specifications. If de-

fective material is produced, it must be detected and corrective action initiated to eliminate or control its source.

Based on these fundamentals, the actual process control operation is developed. It includes the following functions, whose objective is to maintain or reduce company operating costs while product quality is retained or improved to acceptable standards:

1. **Establish and maintain controls** on the accuracy of tooling and gages used in production and inspection, both at initial installation and periodically, to detect wear or change in service. This is the heart of the process control system, since the product can be no better than the tools that produce it and the means used to evaluate it.

2. **Make capability studies of production equipment and processes.** Determine the measurements to be taken, analyze the data produced, and determine action required to correct undesirable conditions.

3. **Establish measurements and process controls to maintain economic control,** and detect entry of any factors that might adversely affect product quality or reliability. Provide adequate written and verbal instructions to personnel performing process control activities. (See Fig. 5-4.)

4. **Review process controls periodically** to adjust for changing conditions and to minimize process control costs.

5. **Assist line manufacturing and other staff engineering** activities in "trouble shooting" to identify and eliminate causes when out-of-control conditions develop.

6. **Design and conduct experiments** to develop process improvements and desirable changes in product design and specifications if either quality or cost of a controlled process is unsatisfactory. Request or implement changes necessary to produce improvement.

Assembly Quality Control

Assembly quality control differs from process quality control for two reasons:

1. An assembly operation is a continuous operation employing

PARTS HISTORY AND FOLLOW-UP CARD

Part Number 16-501-4
Part Name Clutch Band
Material Weldment
Model 71-B, 81-B, Ser.

CODE LETTER

A. Poor Workmanship
B. Careless Handling
C. Faulty Material
D. Tool in Error
E. Wrong Assembly
F. Wrong Material
G. Drawing Error
H. Faulty Vendor Mat.
I. Gage Error
J. Inspection Error
K. Other (Explain in reason for rej.)

No.	Reject Number	Rej. Date	Dept. Rej In	No. Def.	Ord. Qty.	Code	Rework	Use As Is	Scrap	Dept. Resp.
1	11321	12/20	23	16	16	A	X			14
2	14263	2/18	37	1	16	C			X	5-A

REASON FOR REJECTION

1. Distorted in welding, straightened to wrong gage. M. West to re-identify gage racks.
2. Broke on pull test - laminated material. Purchasing advised 2/23 - J. Hart. CRITICAL FAILURE MAY ENDANGER LIFE.

Fig. 5-4

large numbers of people whose efforts are closely related. It is one thing to shut down a machine tool which is out of control but it's vastly different from the operating economics point of view to shut down an assembly line or operation employing six to 600 people because it's producing a poor quality product. One large manufacturer of jet aircraft finds that an hour of downtime on a major airframe jig costs $3,000. Eight hours lost in the assembly operations of a business machines manufacturer is known to cost $24,000. In assembly operations, hesitation in making a decision, or the expenditure of assembly line time to experiment with control of quality, costs large sums of money.

2. Worker attitude affects quality control. If a line worker assembles 200 units a day and is careless or inattentive for only two minutes during the day, he may produce one bad assembly. This will be almost impossible to detect by inspection methods, yet the customer who purchases that one specific assembly will discover it. Multiply the case of the one momentarily careless worker by the number of people employed in assembly operations and obviously an enormous percentage of the output is affected. For example, a producer of small electrical machinery discovered through statistical audit techniques that his assembly employees did their individual jobs properly 98.62 per cent of the time. However, finished assemblies contained an average of 6.8 random defects attributed to assembly workmanship, and customer rejections exceeded 20 per cent!

Assembly quality control must develop, install, and maintain inspection practices and product evaluation techniques that guarantee only an acceptable product is assembled, packaged, and shipped. It includes these functions:

1. **Develop, install, and maintain assembly inspection and analytical procedures** to determine assembly quality levels and assure acceptance of satisfactory product. Insure quality standards applied are compatible with design and detail part requirements.

2. **Develop and utilize economic sampling plans and controls.**

3. **Provide both routine and special feedback of inspection results** to quality control engineering and other interested parties so that corrective action can be taken if necessary.

4. **Develop and implement quality levels and appropriate defect classifications for quality rating** of completed product and packaging compatible with customer requirements and capabilities of the product and assembly processes.

5. **Analyze customer complaints and field reports,** and devise methods of verifying or disproving the existence of such problems in outgoing products. Identify causes and assign responsibility for initiation of corrective action. Evaluate degree of improvement obtained from corrective action as it becomes effective.

Quality Verification and Audit

Consideration must now be given to an anomaly of the quality assurance business. A complete system of quality assurance may exist from product conception to shipment, yet customers complain that they received bad products. How can this be? What is wrong with the inspection systems and quality assurance controls?

The answer is supplied by the quality verification and audit activity whose job it is to inspect the inspectors. Quality audit is an extension of the quality assurance manager's responsibility for controlling results and appraising performance discussed in Chapter Three. In small quality assurance operations, the manager personally performs the quality verification and audit functions. In large, multiplant corporations, it may be necessary to create a staff organization of sizable proportions to carry out these activities.

Regardless of company size, these functions must be performed and not lost in the demands of daily operations. Quality verification and audit functions must:

1. **Develop and utilize inspection, audit, and analytical procedures to verify the quality level of outgoing product.** Insure compatibility of these procedures with customer demands and product specifications.

2. **Develop and utilize inspection, audit, and analytical procedures to verify inspector performance at acceptable levels.**

3. **Develop and utilize inspection, audit, and analytical procedures to evaluate quality performance by individual production operators.**

4. **Evaluate, analyze, and rate audit findings on outgoing product quality,** inspector performance and production operator

quality performance. Issue appropriate reports to management for information and corrective action.

5. **Devise and apply accelerated testing techniques for product life and reliability**, suitably correlated with reliability test programs previously or concurrently carried out by other activities, to provide continuous evaluation of the reliability level of outgoing product.

6. **Cooperate with quality verification programs by other corporate activities** or by outside testing and standards bodies such as the various federal and state government activities, Underwriters Laboratories, and various consumer testing groups, such as Consumers Union and Buyers Laboratories.

7. **Conduct special quality audit and verification investigations requested by quality assurance or top management.**

In quality verification and audit, the last of the check and balance systems required in successful quality assurance is completed. The quality assurance line activities of incoming material quality assurance, process quality control, and assembly quality control are serviced by the quality engineering and vendor quality staff groups. They do the necessary planning and preparation for the "doers" of the line operations. Both line and staff activities are evaluated in turn by quality audit, which results in an independent judgment on the effectiveness of both "doing" and "planning" functions.

CHAPTER SIX

Working With Other Departments

Good inspection and application of the most sophisticated quality control techniques do not assure good quality. Quality must be planned into the product from its conception. Quality plans include good design, processibility, inspection, packaging, shipping, installation, and evaluation of customer reactions. The quality assurance plan includes everyone and every happening within the entire manufacturing and marketing system. Quality must be designed into the product, built into the product, and remain in the product throughout its life expectancy.

In addition to the influence of design and production engineering, covered in earlier chapters, other functions contribute directly to quality, or influence quality by their actions. These include:

Finance and Cost Control Sets the basic attitudes in the company toward control of quality costs.

Production Control Determines inventory levels, storeroom and warehouse practices, and process flows to determine the time limits within which Quality Assurance acts.

Purchasing Determines supplier behavior in providing materials and components at proper quality levels and fair prices through its vendor selection and buying practices.

Line Manufacturing Manufactures parts and assemblies, which may or may not satisfy specifications and meet tolerances within the planned economic limits.

Marketing Determines the quality expectations of the customer, including prices that will be paid for corresponding levels of product quality, and evaluates competitive pressures on quality.

Field Service Installs and demonstrates products after the initial sale, repairs them during their normal life, and feeds back failure information to Quality Assurance and consumer information to Marketing.

Obviously the company's quality image is a complex reflection of interdepartmental relationships. If top management expects the quality assurance system to equip the company with a top quality image, it must control numerous cost-quality, schedule-quality, and personnel conflicts which result from interdepartmental conflicts. Quality assurance people must also understand these relationships and establish a free exchange of information and ideas with the other areas. This requires knowledge of what each group requires from the others.

Finance and Cost Control

Finance and cost control activities are concerned with the flow of cash through the business, and with conserving the company's assets, and seldom if ever think about quality.

From Quality Assurance, Finance and Cost Control wants:

1. **Prompt reports** on budget performance, expenditures, and all other data required to complete financial reports they must issue in turn.

2. **Reasonable cooperation** in establishing budgets and reviewing quality assurance expenditures.

3. **Help** in reducing quality costs such as scrap and rework.

4. **Reasonable care** in maintaining and protecting quality assurance equipment and other assets in the operation's care and control.

5. **If possible, no changes** in product costs and price structures due to quality requirements after the initial pricing is completed.

Quality Assurance wants from Finance and Cost Control:

1. **Consultation** prior to changing budgets, prices, and costing practices that will affect quality assurance operations, the quality of the product, or attitudes toward quality and quality costs within the corporation.

2. **Timely release** of information on quality costs for quality assurance analysis, and cooperation in developing mutually agreeable methods of presentation.

3. **An appreciation** of the necessity for some expenditures on quality factors.

Production Control

Production control is mainly concerned with moving material into the plant, through the process, and out to the customer. They seldom worry about the quality of the material, but only about the speed with which they can move it and the minimum amount of material they can put into process and still meet commitments.

Production Control wants from Quality Assurance:

1. **Decisiveness.** If the material is going to be rejected, reworked, scrapped, used as is, or accepted, decide! Don't hold up the process by being wishy-washy.

2. **Information.** Once the decision is made, inform the affected production control people so they can replace the material or arrange for rework, as required, and get production rolling again.

3. **Consistency.** If the product is accepted, try not to reject it two days later when nothing has happened to it to change its condition.

4. **Understanding.** The need to produce the product in order to keep the business going.

Quality Assurance wants from Production Control:

1. **Time.** Inventory levels cannot be cut back so far, suppliers placed on such short lead times, and customer delivery commitments set so tightly that there is no time for adequate inspection and possible rejection to assure quality.

2. **Good stores and warehouse practices** to prevent quality deterioration of stores material or product.

3. **Good material handling practices** to prevent damage and loss of quality.

4. **Honesty in observing quality assurance procedures and controls.** In particular, expediters bypassing inspection points or "stealing" rejected material.

Purchasing

The area of vendor selection and vendor relationships is a source of conflict in every company. Many quality control people have difficulty recognizing the realities of life with vendors. If there is only one source available for a particular item, why criticize the buyer for using that source despite its poor quality record? Why doesn't Quality Assurance make a positive contribution and help the vendor improve its quality?

Purchasing desires from Quality Assurance:

1. **Reliable data** furnished promptly in a mutually useful form on the results of receiving inspection.

2. **Prompt and timely completion of inspection of vendor material** and components, whether at source or on receipt, and the speedy release of acceptable material to the plant.

3. **Understanding of purchasing economics,** including a good grasp of the fact that, sooner or later, the company pays for "no-charge" rework or scrapping by the vendor.
4. **Realistic vendor rating and evaluation** that is meaningful and useful to the buyer, and capable of substantiation to the vendor.
5. **Accurate vendor quality surveys** that are useful, and conducted by competent and tactful people, and reasonably final.
6. **Assistance for vendors** with quality problems who request help in good faith.
7. **Discussion of vendor problems** between Purchasing and Quality Assurance *prior to discussion with top management.*

Quality Assurance needs from Purchasing:

1. **Understanding the need to pay for quality** and not squeeze vendors on price to the point where quality disappears from the vendor's product.
2. **Prompt notification to the vendor when his quality is not acceptable,** and pressure for corrective action and improvement.
3. **Purchasing cooperation in vendor rating and vendor quality survey programs,** if these are instituted.
4. **Scheduling of vendor shipments to provide sufficient time for inspection and quality evaluation,** either at source or on receipt.
5. **Cooperation in establishing source inspection at vendors if required,** with an understanding that source inspection is for the company's benefit and not intended to bail out a vendor with problems of his own making that he can not or has not corrected.

Line Manufacturing

Dominating the relationship between Line Manufacturing and Quality Assurance is the human problem of "one-up." Invariably, the quality assurance man is dealing with a line man one step above him in the hierarchy of the company. Thus the *hourly rated inspector* customarily copes with the *salaried foreman*, the *inspection foreman* works with the *line general foreman*, etc. Only at the top, where (we hope) the quality assurance manager works with the manufacturing manager, do equals meet. This places serious psychological burdens on these relationships. The line man resents dealing with his inferiors, particularly when they appear to frustrate his desire to produce. The quality assurance people resent this attitude on the part of people they regard as their technical inferiors, who, through little or no genuine achievement on their part, have won a higher spot in the organization.

Unless great care is used, we find line people "bypassing" the inspection people they are supposed to deal with. Instead, the production men try to approach the superiors of these inspectors whom the line men feel are their equals. Much of this "bypassing" which is a sore point with quality assurance people, arises from the psychology of the line, as does the resentment felt by Quality Assurance, rather than from the urge to move production over the wishes of lower quality echelons. It takes wise management to keep this situation in bounds without creating too much friction.

These are the legitimate needs of Line Manufacturing from Quality Assurance:

1. **Responsible and accurate inspection,** rendered on a timely basis without unduly delaying production, and with the courage to acknowledge inspection errors when they do occur and to assume the blame.
2. **Prompt and firm decisions** not subject to daily or hourly change.
3. **Assistance in moving production.**
4. **Cooperation in trouble shooting quality problems,** particularly if statistical skills can be of help.
5. **Understanding that most defects are not controllable** by the operator and his line superiors, but result from the work of staff groups.

Quality Assurance needs from Line Manufacturing:

1. **Acceptance of the basic line responsibility for quality,** without attempting to foist it on the inspectors.

2. **Responsible handling of rework and corrective action** responsibilities when assigned, rather than attempting to shunt them off to other areas, within or without Manufacturing.

3. **Cooperation and reasonable working relationships** and, in particular, not abusing inspection people, verbally or physically.

Marketing

The company needs to determine the level of quality the customer desires. This responsibility is usually assigned to the marketing or sales activity.

Marketing needs from Quality Assurance include:

1. **A quality product all the time** to meet the consumer demands for consistent quality.
2. **Assistance in pacifying the irate customer.**
3. **Quality evaluation of competitive products.**
4. **Analysis of field failures,** particularly in regard to the level of customer expectations. Did the customer want more than the product was capable of delivering?

Quality Assurance wants from Marketing:

1. **Information on customer requirements,** particularly those that fall outside the realm of physical and engineering specifications.
2. **Information on the success the customer has** in applying products and utilizing them.
3. **Timely receipt of this information,** at the time the product is conceived, and not months after initial sales and shipment.

Field Service

In a sense, field service is merely an extension of the quality assurance approach in another area. This is particularly true if the product requires periodic maintenance. In such cases, it is necessary to inspect the product, note and correct problems and failures, and transmit this information to the responsible parties for corrective action. This is the same process we defined as the basic feedback loop for quality assurance in the plant. It follows that field service requirements from Quality Assurance are similar to Quality Assurance's needs from other areas:

1. **Information on changes in the product** which affect customer performance and serviceability, including all those little process changes made, usually, for cost reduction purposes which "don't really affect the product."
2. **Acceptance of responsibility** and a genuine effort to verify field problems in plant.
3. **Assistance in getting corrective action** to overcome field problems.

On the other hand, Quality Assurance needs help from Field Service:

1. **Reliable data on repairs and failures,** both in and out of warranty, and classified by cause, such as: abuse and accident, serviceman error, product failure, damage in transit, etc.
2. **Recognition of the possibility of servicemen's "pet peeves" biasing the data,** and action to eliminate such problems when discovered.
3. **A system of evaluating applications.**
4. **Facts on service performance** of competitive products.

Personnel and Training

Many quality control people erroneously believe that only they are qualified to select and train quality control personnel, and resist efforts by personnel people to perform this function. This is nonsense. Let the trained personnel people screen the drunks, psychological cases, and other problem people prior to presenting qualified candidates for final selection. Also, don't waste valuable quality assurance manpower indoctrinating new employees in company-wide practices. Let Training do it.

To do their job, Personnel and Training need from Quality Assurance:

1. **An understanding of personnel administration requirements,** including graceful compliance with company policies and procedures.
2. **Time to do their job,** and not a demand for a man the day he is required. Give Personnel ample notice.
3. **Cooperate in developing a mutually agreeable training program.** In fact, Training may get part of the job done under one of the federal or state government-sponsored training programs at no charge to the company.

Quality Assurance needs from Personnel and Training:

1. **Well-screened, qualified candidates.**
2. **Evaluation of area wage rates** and personnel practices so that the company is competitive, attracting and retaining good people.
3. **Sound and consistent advice on personnel practices** and labor relations problems.
4. **Stress on quality practices in selection and training** of all people to build a quality attitude throughout the company.

CHAPTER SEVEN

Budgeting and Cost Reduction

Management's job is to control the company's expenditures in terms of time and capital so that the cost of doing business is less than the income from sales, and the company makes a profit. Time is represented by dollars paid to employees and capital represents dollars provided to build the plant, and pay the operating costs to produce and market the product. The flow of these dollars must be efficiently controlled.

Dollar Control Concepts

Within a manufacturing activity, each manager is responsible for controlling the flow and timing of certain types and amounts of dollar expenditures. Anyone proposing changes in the management structure of a business must be prepared to accept the responsibility for changing these flows and timing elements. Change or innovation cannot occur without altering expenditure patterns. Top management welcomes innovation, for it has learned it is profitable. Its books indicate exactly how past innovations have paid off. This is possible because of the changes in accounting methods which have permitted better analysis, identification, and control of costs. These changes were not brought about only by accountants. Often the advocates of a tool or technique had to seek and obtain the establishment of new accounting practices which would demonstrate the cost advantages of their new proposal.

Therefore, anyone advocating a quality assurance system must prove that the system will help produce the product to specification, on schedule, at or below established cost standards, and will contribute to the long-term health of the business. If it does not do this, there is no justification for a quality assurance system.

Quality Costs

Several authorities have prepared long lists of detailed quality costs. Some are referred to in the bibliography. All these listings can be broken down into three main groupings, which are:

1. **Cost of operation**—the cost of the things Quality Assurance does.
2. **Cost of goofing**—internal costs incurred within the business due to scrap and rework, and measures taken to eliminate or reduce these problems.
3. **Cost of the goofs you missed**—external costs due to warranty and policy adjustments, liability insurance, lawsuits, and similar costs due to quality failures after the product leaves point of manufacture or service is performed.

The sum of these costs is the total quality cost of the business. It is astonishing to discover how few companies know accurately what their total quality costs are.

Budgeting the Quality Function

The quality assurance budget is management's formal dollar commitment to the plans and programs for quality control and quality cost reduction. Budgets are needed to:

1. **Set up targets** at which to aim, and to measure the accuracy of the aim and the degree of attainment.

2. **Force proper planning** of the most economical expenditure of dollars for labor, materials, and other expenses.

3. **Report variances** to management between budget standards and actual performance, so that investigation and corrective action are initiated.

4. **Define areas** of financial and other responsibilities.

There are basic weaknesses in some budget plans, however, which must be avoided by planners establishing budgets and operating men working with them. These weaknesses include:

1. **Indecisiveness.** The organization is in a continuing state of flux, usually due to some executive's compulsion to constantly tinker with assignments or responsibilities. This makes budgets worthless for comparative purposes because they cannot keep up with the changes.

2. **Rigidity.** Budgets must have sufficient flexibility to compensate for normal changes in the company.

3. **Incompleteness.** Partial budgets expose operating executives to the temptation of juggling expenditures into unbudgeted areas.

4. **Complexity.** The budget installation process takes so long or is so complex that management interest is lost before results are obtained.

5. **Top secret.** The budget is the personal property of one man or a small group, and no one else knows or cares about it.

The Budgets Executives Forum breaks down budgets into the following four steps:

1. **Premising.** The predictive function, involving a long and careful look into the future of the business.

2. **Planning.** The function of establishing definite programs to translate premises to realities.

3. **Forecasting.** The function of expressing planning results in dollars and statistical figures.

4. **Budgeting.** This reduces premises, plans and forecasts to operating levels in terms of anticipated and actual dollar expenditures, measuring results against objectives.

It is apparent that budgeting is merely a formal expression, in terms of dollars, of those management steps discussed in Chapter Three which are required to successfully administer the quality assurance function. There should be no logical objection by quality assurance people to participating in, and working under, a system of budgetary control. In fact, such objections indicate either an immature attitude, or the inability of the objector to determine the complete scope of his operations and their probable costs. Neither attitude can be permitted if the quality assurance operation is to be successful.

Budgets establish requirements for people, facilities, and equipment. These requirements are determined by an activity estimate predicted from sales forecasts, anticipated technological advances, and forecasted changes in customer demands. In areas such as warranty and policy expense forecasting, attention must be paid to historical data in estimating these future expenses. Build or buy decisions will also have a major effect on budget forecasts.

In quality assurance areas, decisions may involve weighing the alternatives of purchasing environmental and laboratory testing services, or creating these facilities; utilizing temporary personnel services for vacation and peak-load demands or permanently increasing the staff; in-house designing and building gages and test equipment or purchasing this equipment. Each decision can involve the expenditure of hundreds of thousands of dollars, for people, facilities, and equipment.

Budgets are normally prepared for a one-year period and reviewed and revised quarterly. Variance reports are usually issued on a weekly or monthly basis. Larger companies are now beginning to develop tentative budgets for five to ten years ahead as a base for profit planning.

Quality Cost Reduction Programs

Quality cost reductions must be planned. As a starting point, consider all the elements in quality expenses listed below, and appraise the cost reduction potential of each item.

CHECK LIST FOR APPRAISING QUALITY ASSURANCE EXPENSE REDUCTION POTENTIAL[1]

1. **Total Administrative Cost—determined by:**
   a. Scope and complexity of work supervised.
   b. Number of levels of supervision.
   c. Number of people supervised.
   d. Size of work area supervised.
   e. Physical proximity of work areas supervised.
   f. Maturity and stability of organization.
   g. Maturity and stability of product.
   h. Experience and background of supervisors.

2. **Total Quality Systems Planning Costs—determined by** the amount and effectiveness of the quality engineering effort. This can be measured by evaluating the number of things done by Quality Engineering, such as:
   a. Number of test procedures written, and total pages included.
   b. Value of test equipment designed.
   c. Number of vendor or customer contact trips.
   d. Number of quality problems followed by each engineer.
   e. Number of engineering information requests written.
   f. Number of corrective action requests written.
   g. Time spent in meetings.
   h. Time spent in trouble shooting.
   i. Number of letters or memos written.
   j. Number of quality cost reduction projects being pursued.
   k. Number of statistical problems handled.

[1] Developed by Chester Gadzinski, President, Reliability Dynamics Institute.

l. Extent of quality audit assignments.
m. Idle time as determined by work sampling.

The effectiveness of the quality engineering effort can be measured by the ability of the test and inspection plan to discriminate efficiently between acceptable and unacceptable products. This can be evaluated by:

a. Customer complaints.
b. Factory failures.
c. Number of changes made to inspection and test procedures.
d. Number of changes made to inspection and test equipment.
e. Downtime for lack of procedures or equipment.
f. Time spent trouble shooting finished product.
g. Budget performance.
h. Schedule performance.
i. Elimination of duplicate tests through total test planning. (This should include use of vendor inspection and test results to minimize receiving inspection and test.)

3. **Construction and Maintenance Costs of Inspection and Test Equipment—evaluated by:**

a. Value of equipment produced divided by the number of people required to produce it.
b. Number of characteristics planned to be checked divided by the number of people required to check them.
c. Ratio of preplanned maintenance time versus unplanned repair time.
d. Ratio of made-in-plant special purpose equipment to purchased multipurpose equipment.

Costs of calibration of inspection and test equipment—determined by the number of pieces of equipment calibrated times the frequency of calibration. Scheduling of calibration is based on such factors as:

a. Severity of environment.
b. Delicacy of equipment.
c. Severity of use.

d. Frequency of use.
e. Accuracy of measurement required.
f. Past performance history.
g. Importance of condition or characteristic controlled.

4. **Inspection and Test Costs—evaluated by:**

a. Receiving inspection and tests.
   1. Ratio of receiving inspection and test costs to value of incoming material.
   2. Lots or units of product handled by each inspector.
   3. Time in processing product through receiving inspection.
   4. Productive versus nonproductive time as determined by work sampling.

b. In-process inspection and test.
   1. Ratio of inspection and test to direct labor.
   2. Lots or units of product handled by each inspector.
   3. Time in processing product through inspection and test stations.
   4. Productive versus nonproductive time as determined by work sampling.

c. Assembly inspection and test (including packaging inspection).
   1. Ratio of inspection and test to direct labor.
   2. Lots or units of product handled by each inspector.
   3. Time in processing product through inspection stations.
   4. Productive versus nonproductive time as measured by work sampling.
   5. Over or under packaging as determined by customer complaints and controlled trial shipments.

5. **Tool Inspection Costs—evaluated as follows:**

a. Ratio of inspection to toolroom labor.
b. Lots or units of tools handled by each inspector.
c. Delays in inspection, including production time lost.
d. Number of tools rejected in-process after acceptance by tool inspection.

e. Productive versus nonproductive time as measured by work sampling.

6. Miscellaneous Potentials for Excessive Expense:

a. Inefficient data processing.
b. Inefficient acceptance sampling.
c. Inefficient control sampling.
d. All cases of 100 per cent inspection.
e. Scrap disposal systems—is it sorted and sold for maximum economic value?

7. Miscellaneous Potentials for Expense Reduction:

a. Organizational structure changes.
b. Increased inspection and test automation.
c. Work factor studies.

Changes in any of these items will affect costs. In evaluating such cost changes, remember that consideration should be given to determine what costs would disappear if there were no defects whatever.

CHAPTER EIGHT

Firing Line Strategy

The quality assurance plan has now been developed. The areas of responsibilities and authority have been assigned, and all quality relationships thought out. Costs and budgets have been established. Now, it is necessary to make the plan work.

Immediately two possibilities are apparent: (1) The plan works perfectly, is accepted by every one involved in its operation, and is a resounding success. This possibility can be safely ignored, because it has never happened and probably never will. (2) There is much cursing and tearing of hair; problems mount; top management becomes progressively nasty about quality problems hindering production; and the quality assurance manager contemplates updating his resumé and refreshing his contacts with executive search organizations. This is the normal way a quality assurance program starts. The urgent need is to bring order out of chaos and get on with the plan. How?

Don't panic! In the long-ago peaceful days when the quality assurance plan was worked out, one of the things accomplished was to classify quality characteristics and probable failures of the product by level of importance. This was covered in the detailed functions of preproduction planning in Chapter Five. Use this classification to analyze the problems reported from line operations before you get started on them.

Operations on the Firing Line

When the inevitable phone calls pour into the quality assurance offices, or the worried line supervisors appear in person, ask these questions:

Has this problem occurred before? If so, what was done about it, who did it, and what were the results?

Is this problem holding up production?

Is someone else doing something to correct the problem? If so, who, and what is he doing about it?

How did the new quality assurance operation contribute to the problem, if it did?

From the answers obtained to these four questions, it is possible to judge the urgency of the situation and in many cases reduce the problem to the status of a telephone call. If it appears that action has already been initiated, or should be initiated in another area, a telephone call to the party concerned, a suitable note for a later follow-up call to insure action is taken, and a few consoling words to the man reporting the problem may be all that is required. If this is the case, forget it until follow-up is required. Don't waste time on these minor problems of daily operations but reserve time, talent, and manpower for problems that indicate the system is in trouble. If the quality assurance plan has created the problem or, much worse, does not provide for the situation which has appeared, *move!* This is no fire to fight! This is a situation which may imperil the whole program. *Move!* But first ask two questions. What action is needed? What method of action is indicated? Gather the data required to answer the following:

First. Assign skilled, technically qualified people on the job with the line supervisor. Discuss the situation with the inspector and the inspection foreman, and respect their opinions and conclusions. They may be in error, but remember the odds are they know a great deal more about the job and the specific quality problem than anyone in the organization.

Second. Be sure that the job is being run as required by process instructions and standards, and that inspection is being applied as planned. Are the gages accurate? Are the blueprints current? Has anything about the job, including such items as the time study standard or incentive rate, been deliberately changed in the past few days?

Third. If no deliberate change was induced in the process, has an unintentional change been made? Check out any available statistics, including those accumulated by the line organization, to see if any trend is detectable. If no trend is apparent, work backward from the problem area, investigating each process and procedure for a clue as to what changed to produce the bad product.

This change must fall in one of two categories: There has been an actual physical change in the product; or standards by which the product is evaluated have been changed. In the first case, determine the responsible area in the organization to make the correction and apply pressure on them to do so. If the evaluation standards have changed, first decide if the change is justified. If not, rescind it. If it is, notify the people involved of the change, if they were not notified earlier; and put on pressure for change just as if asking for corrective action on a product drift problem.

Finally, evaluate the quality assurance plan in terms of the problem situation and revise the plan as necessary.

Line-Staff Relationships

Quality Assurance is a staff organization in almost any company plan. This is a proper classification because it does not, through its own personnel or actions, contribute directly to the manufacture of the product nor the actual selling in the market place.

However, many people often overlook the fact that an internal line and staff functional division exists in the quality assurance operation. The line function consists of the inspection personnel, and their supervision, who physically handle and inspect the product in in-coming process and final inspection, and gather the data collected through these inspections. The staff is those people who plan and support the inspection activities and analyze the accumulated data.

Basic organizational principles apply to separating quality engineering from inspection functions. If inspection supervision is responsible for the inspectors' activities, quality assurance engineers cannot wander around the floor telling inspectors and line people what to do. Quality engineers must understand and accept the *selling role* in implementing their ideas, rather than the *telling role* of direct supervision.

One-Up-Man-Ship

A major operating problem in Quality Assurance results from the clash in status levels between quality assurance personnel and the line manufacturing organization. For example, the quality assurance inspector, a member of the hourly wage worker group, deals with the production foreman, a salaried employee who normally supervises hourly wage workers. The inspection foreman or general foreman usually deals with a manufacturing superintendent. Thus, at all levels inspection people are dealing with line manufacturing personnel at least one level above them in the company's organization. As a result, line people assume overbearing attitudes, and want to deal with higher levels in the quality assurance organization. This irritates the quality assurance people, who regard such moves by line people as attacks on quality assurance status.

From a practical point of view, this one-up problem can be handled in two ways. Higher echelons in Quality Assurance can rigorously insist on line people dealing with established levels in the quality organization. If done impersonally, the point can be put over without offending line feelings. Or, raise the status of the quality assurance people. This can be done simply and inexpensively by providing inspectors with desks and working areas equivalent to those of the line foremen, giving inspection foremen such status symbols as reserved parking spaces, name plates on desks, etc., similar to those enjoyed by higher level manufacturing supervision. In some cases, inspectors have been taken out of union hourly groups and placed on salary to combat this situation.

Control Through Respect and Responsibility

The one-up problem furnishes additional reason for recognition of the prime requirement for successful quality operations in a company. This requirement is that the quality assurance activity command the respect of all other elements in the organization and accept full responsibility for any errors it makes or causes others to make. In Chapter One we defined total quality assurance as a broad set of policies applied by all managers in the company, with the service assistance of a staff function charged with policy development and administration in quality manners. Obviously, if all managers apply broad policies developed by a staff group, the degree of sincere application will be controlled by the reactions of all managers to the quality assurance staff.

Sincere application is distinct from lip service rendered because top management gives orders to assure quality. This is obtained only when other members of management are convinced that Quality Assurance knows its job and does it well; that it gives good advice and reliable data; works hard for the mutual needs of the company; and supports the rest of the organization. Office politics does not advance the acceptance of quality assurance, nor does a nine-to-five approach to the job.

Inspection Tools and Techniques

If good advice and reliable data are presented, there must be accurate means employed to gather such data. In brief, the first basic assumption in Chapter Three (that information furnished by inspection is accurate and reliable) must be factually assured. The inspection tools and techniques used to gather data must be equally accurate and reliable, for the data is no better than the means employed to accumulate it. But excessive costs cannot be incurred to develop overly precise tools and techniques yielding more accurate data than is required.

This text cannot catalog all the tools and techniques available for inspection purposes. Sources of information are noted below for each major area.

1. *Basic Measuring Instruments* Rules, scales, micrometers and similar devices, surface plate accessories and other universal hand-held dimensional checking devices. Refer to the catalogs of such companies as Brown & Sharpe Mfg. Co., the L. S. Starrett Co., and the Lufkin Rule Company.

2. *Basic Gaging Devices* Plug and ring gages, snap gages, thread comparators, pin gages, dial indicators, and accessories. Refer to Federal Products Corporation, Size Control Company, B. C. Ames Company, or Taft-Pierce.

3. *Calibration Equipment—Mechanical* Electronic comparators, master micrometers, measuring microscopes, and gage blocks. Refer to Pratt & Whitney Division of Fairbanks Whitney, the Sheffield Corporation, Brown & Sharpe Mfg. Co., Gaertner Scientific Corporation, and Federal Products Corporation.

4. *Calibration Equipment—Electrical and Electronic* Usually produced to special order and adapted to the user's special requirements. Standard units are made by such concerns as Leeds & Northrup Co., Beckman Instruments, Inc., Radio Frequency Laboratories, Inc., and the large industrial instrument suppliers such as General Electric Company.

5. *Optical Comparators* Furnished by Bausch & Lomb, Inc., Optical Gaging Products, Inc., Kollmorgen Corporation, Nikon, Inc., and Stocker & Yale Inc.

6. *Nondestructive Test Equipment* X-ray radiography, ultrasonic, and infrared examination of parts and materials supplied by such companies as General Electric Company, Eastman Kodak, Picker X-Ray Corp., Krautkamer Ultrasonics, Inc., Automation Industries, Inc., or Magnaflux Corporation.

7. *Environmental Test Equipment* Usually produced to order for each application. Basic units are supplied by such organizations as the Bethlehem Corporation, Industrial Products Subdivision of AVCO, and Cincinnati Sub-Zero Products.

8. *Physical, Chemical, and Metallographic Test and Laboratory Equipment* Usually obtained from the large scientific supply houses such as Central Scientific, Harshaw's, etc. Specific pieces of equipment are supplied by certain companies, such as tensile testers by Tinius-Olsen, spring testers by Hunter Spring Company, and tear-testing units by Thwing-Albert Instrument Co.

In an efficient total quality assurance operation, it is the specific responsibility of at least one engineer to maintain a complete file of manufacturer's catalogs, devote a good portion of his time to regular contacts with salesmen and manufacturers' agents, and serve as a consultant on inspection equipment to other company areas.

As a general reference, one of the best sources of information on new inspection and test tools and techniques is the magazine *Quality Assurance* published by the Hitchcock Publishing Company. In the special fields of environmental, nondestructive, and laboratory testing, one must refer to the professional journals published in each field.

Automatic Inspection

Automation will make great changes in inspection operations. These changes are already affecting three broad areas:

First. Increased use of automatic sorting of product in 100 per cent acceptance inspection. This use of automatic inspection overcomes the great disadvantage of 100 per cent inspection by manual methods, since it eliminates the human error which usually limits 100 per cent inspection accuracy to 85 per cent or less defect detection.

Second. Automatic inspection equipment provides automatically recorded and, in some cases, analyzed data on a far more timely basis than would otherwise be available.

Third. Automatic inspection units are used to close the feedback loop in process control, automatically inspecting parts produced, determining trend of variation, and adjusting the process to compensate for these trends and prevent production of defects.

Successful applications have been made in all three fields. Equipment manufacturers, such as Federal Products Corporation or Sheffield Corporation, produce automatic sorting equipment, complete with recording devices. In the area of business and office equipment manufacturing, such leaders as Burroughs Corporation, Olivetti-Underwood Corporation, and Smith-Corona Marchant have placed much of the final inspection of business machines on automatic, tape-programed testers. International Business Machines Corporation has installed input devices on assembly inspector work stations, so that an inspector's data is recorded in, and analyzed by, a computer while the inspector is doing his assigned tasks. The engine block machining lines of General Motors and Ford Motor Company incorporate automatic gaging equipment engineered to automatically adjust tools as they wear and to shut the machine down and call the setup man when a situation exists which the machine cannot correct. The Convair Division of General Dynamics Corporation is utilizing closed-circuit television to inspect large aircraft and missile parts for dimensional accuracy. Fairchild Semiconductor Corporation uses automatic testing procedures on finished transistors, producing punched cards of the results for subsequent data processing at the same time the test is run.

The major deterrent to automatic inspection is the high initial cost. Even the simplest go- no-go sorting unit will cost $2,000 or $3,000, while fully automated process control equipment may exceed $100,000 per installation. In addition, the automatic equipment is relatively inflexible. Product redesign may cause long and expensive alterations in the automatic inspection equipment, or even early scrapping before the equipment has paid off.

Nevertheless, the potential cost savings and greater inspection accuracy and defect detection efficiency guarantee continued expansion in this field. The total quality assurance operation must keep in touch and be prepared to do its own pioneering in this field.

Inspector Training and Control

The constant change in inspection techniques and the need for reliable data from inspectors requires a planned program for inspector training. An initial "after-hire" training program is not sufficient, but consideration must be given to continued programs to keep inspectors abreast of technological improvements and familiar with product changes.

At a minimum, initial training must include:

1. Blueprint reading and company drafting practices.
2. Fundamental shop mathematics.
3. Basic manufacturing techniques used by the company.
4. Product familiarization.
5. Use and care of inspection equipment.
6. Basic shop inspection and quality control procedures, including control charts and sampling plans used.

It is not necessary to run every new inspector through each subject. A series of qualifying tests can be used and passing a test automatically excuses a man from the subject. It is also wise to run new salaried technical people through this course, so they have a sound foundation in the company's inspection techniques and practices.

The quality of inspector performance must be controlled. This involves performance rating and appraisal with corrective training to build up weak spots, regular short training courses to introduce a new product or process to the inspection work force, and in- or out-plant training of selected individuals for promotion to higher level jobs in the organization. In addition, it is essential to insure that physical defects do not affect inspection efficiency. Periodic eye tests should be given to all quality control inspectors and technical personnel. People involved in color-matching, noise detection, alignment checks, and other specialized tasks should be given appropriate tests for color-sensing and color-blindness, hearing, depth perception, etc. These tests should be given to inspectors, inspection supervisors, quality control engineers, and even the quality assurance manager. Anybody unwilling to take or unable to pass these tests has no business exercising judgment in the areas involved.

Conflicts of Interest

In Chapter Five, we touched briefly on the subject of conflicts of interest. This is a problem in all quality assurance operations areas. Even the lowliest inspector is in a position to pay off his friends and damage his enemies. The quality analyst can slant his reports to favor the line supervisor he likes. A favored industrial engineer's cost reduction program can be aided by low inspection requirements and quality will be imperiled.

All of these favors have one thing in common. They do not involve theft, or misappropriation of company funds. They are nonfinancial. As a result, many people excuse their participation in such deals on the basis that it doesn't really hurt the firm. Obviously this is not true.

The first step in fighting conflicts of interest is to recognize they exist, and be alert to detect them. A determined effort should be made to build inspector and engineer loyalty to the company and the quality assurance operation, rather than developing ties with the departments to which they are assigned or work in.

Next, Quality Assurance should have a firm and well-publicized policy for dealing with this problem, with immunity for no one, not even the quality assurance manager. If a case does occur, it should be dealt with promptly, firmly, and publicly, so that all personnel are aware of the consequences of such actions. In addition, temptations should be minimized by job rotation practices, continual review of rejection dispositions, and careful analysis of reports.

Quality assurance supervision must be acquainted with their people. They should know who rides in what car pool, who has received any unusual gifts or favors outside the plant, who has family or friendship ties in other areas, and be on the alert for the possibility of conflict situations occurring.

Quality in Distributing

Quality requirements exist in the distribution process just as they do in the manufacturing process, but are often not recognized. Packaging, point-of-sale displays, even the appearance of company premises and equipment in branch sales operations, affect the company's quality image. Total quality assurance demands that the distribution quality situation be carefully reviewed at periodic intervals and controlled by audit techniques. It does not follow that Quality Assurance will be called on to run this audit. It must be prepared, however, to counsel the marketing group on efficient and accurate ways to control distribution quality.

One of the most overlooked areas in the total quality picture is the consumer goods field. Customer attitude may make a tremendous difference in product reception and evaluation. This attitude is largely determined by the customer's experiences immediately prior to and after the sale. An excellent illustration is the experience of any major oil company with the impact of restroom cleanliness on its customers, particularly women. The oil companies have found it takes only one bad experience with a restroom to permanently drive away a woman customer. Quality in distribution therefore must be planned, audited, and controlled.

Quality After-Sale Techniques

Quality after-sale techniques fall into two specific areas. One involves the gathering of reliable and unbiased data on customer reaction to the product. The second is concerned with answering customer complaints in a manner calculated to maintain the company quality image.

The first area, if properly handled, is the best source of data for corrective action. No matter how many failures Quality Assurance may induce in testing at the plant, some skeptic in Engineering or management will always object to the artificiality of the test. When the product fails in the customer's hands, these objections vanish.

Quality Assurance should obtain and analyze the following data on product problems and failures after sale:

Type of failure—what broke or went "Boom!"?
Effect of failure on product—what happened?
Repair or correction made—how was it fixed?
Cost of repair or correction—to evaluate seriousness.
Who paid for repair—in warranty, customer expense, what?
Environmental conditions at time of failure.
Operating time elapsed to failure.

Then, an effort should be made to duplicate the problem in controlled conditions, to determine the probable cause and develop inspection controls against future occurrences.

The second area, answering customer complaints, is often not assigned to Quality Assurance. However, quality assurance personnel should be interested in this area, at least on an audit information basis, to insure that information going out to disgruntled customers squares with the total quality image of the concern as closely as possible.

CHAPTER NINE

Statistical Methods

Data concerning any problem, series of events, or set of occurrences, inside or outside of a factory or business situation, will show variation. If measurements are taken and recorded of such data, the numbers used in recording will be found to vary. Variation is found in absentee rates, production output figures, accounting figures, process control readings, room temperatures, or any other set of numbers developed from an industrial process. In fact, since there is no known type of industrial process in which variation is not present, failure to find variation in recorded data indicates errors in measurement and recording.

Fluctuations in recorded data are caused by large numbers of minute differences in the process being observed. These are due to differences in materials, ambient conditions, performance of people, and changes in equipment. Most of these differences are extremely small and, combined, cause continuous minor fluctuations in the data known as *normal* or *natural* variation. At times, however, there is a large variation, causing the pattern to fluctuate in an *abnormal* or *unnatural* manner. These large variations are caused by changes in operators, equipment, or materials and are identifiable by means of simple mathematical calculations based on statistical laws. Once identified, steps can be taken to determine the cause of these large variations. Thus, the basic purpose of statistical methods in the total quality assurance function is to detect significant departures from normal operations, determine the causes thereof, and initiate appropriate action.

Frequency Distributions

Variations as such are not the only statistical phenomena observable in the world. If a large number of observations are taken of some physical characteristic, such as the weight of ten-year-old male children, these measurements will tend to group themselves around some central value with a certain amount of variation on each side. This grouping is called a *frequency distribution.* It can also be observed that if the process producing these measurements is unchanged, the distribution tends to have certain fixed characteristics. On the other hand, if the process changes, so do the characteristics of the frequency distribution.

Two sets of statistical phenomena, distribution and fluctuation, are closely related. *A distribution is a composite mass of fluctuations; fluctuations occur within the limits of a distribution.* Therefore it is possible to establish statistical limits for fluctuations, derived from the distributions, when there are no abnormal or unnatural causes affecting the process.

In summary:

1. **Everything varies.**
2. **Individuals are unpredictable, but**
3. **Groups of individuals from a system not affected by abnormal causes tend to be predictable.**

Frequency distributions (see Fig. 9-1) have three useful characteristics which can be analyzed for information:

1. **Center, or average value.**
2. **Spread, width, or dispersion.**
3. **Shape.**

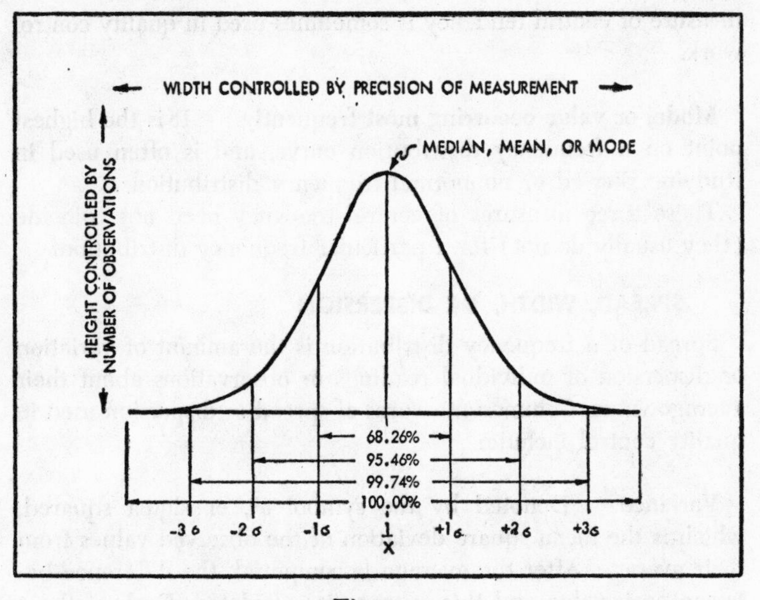

Fig. 9-1

Each of these characteristics can be described by standard statistical techniques, giving a means of measurement.

CENTER, OR AVERAGE VALUE

Observations plotted in the form of a frequency distribution tend to cluster around some central value. This point around which the readings tend to cluster is called the "central value." It can be established mathematically by one of three common measures:

Arithmetic mean, or average All observed values are added together and divided by the number of observations to establish this average, which is almost universally used in quality control work. It is commonly denoted by the symbol "$\bar{X}$."

Median, or most central observed value It is found by arranging the observed readings in order of magnitude and identifying the center reading. This, in a series of seventeen observations, would be the ninth reading in order of magnitude. This measure of central tendency is sometimes used in quality control work.

Mode, or value occurring most frequently It is the highest point on a frequency distribution curve, and is often used in studying skewed or nonnormal frequency distributions.

These three measures of central tendency need not coincide (they usually do not) for a particular frequency distribution.

SPREAD, WIDTH, OR DISPERSION

Spread of a frequency distribution is the amount of variation or dispersion of individual readings or observations about their average value. Common measures of spread or dispersion used in quality control include:

Variance Denoted by the symbol σ^2, or sigma squared, which is the mean square deviation of the observed values from their average. After the average is computed, the difference between each value and this average is calculated. Each of these differences is squared, the squares totaled, and this total divided by the number of values.

Standard deviation Denoted by the symbol σ, or sigma, which is the square root of the variance as calculated above, or the root mean square derivation of values from the average. It is computed by simply taking the square root of the variance, as calculated above.

Range Denoted by the symbol R, is the difference between the highest observed value and the lowest observed value in a frequency distribution.

SHAPE

After a frequency distribution is plotted, it will have a certain profile or shape. Actual distributions do not precisely resemble the symmetrical curves of a textbook, but by approximation they can be assigned to categories for classification and analysis. These classifications include the following:

The normal distribution (also referred to as the normal curve or bell-shaped curve).
Symmetrical distributions which are not normal.
Nonsymmetrical or skewed distributions.
Distributions with multiple (two or more) peaks.

The normal distribution is important in quality control, since it underlies the basic theory of control charts. Even though a given distribution may not precisely fit the normal curve established by the mathematical definition of normal distribution, it often is reasonably similar and can be used to establish control limits. There are also mathematical tests available to test given sets of data for normality, such as the chi-square test and measures of skewness and kurtosis.

Control Charts—Theory and Practice

Using statistical laws, it is possible to calculate limits of distribution for data obtained from a normal population or process which is subject only to natural variation. These limits can be plotted in chart form, regular measurements made and plotted on the chart, and the chart evaluated in terms of data points within and without the limits. Points falling outside the limits indicate the process is being influenced by nonnormal causes and signal a need for investigation and correction. This is the basic and simple purpose of a control chart in quality control practice.

Many different kinds of data can be plotted on a control chart. However, certain types of data are much more sensitive than others in detecting nonnormal variations in a process. In order of decreasing sensitivity, these include:

Ranges of small groups (three to ten) of measurements.
Averages, particularly of small groups.
Percentages.
Individual observations.

The usual control chart combines the two most sensitive kinds of data, averages and ranges, and is referred to as an *average and range* or $\overline{X}$ *and R* (pronounced *X-bar* and *R*) chart. Next most widely used is the *p-chart* using percentages. There are many other versions of control charts, but the $\overline{X}$ and *R* and *p* are most widely used. (See Fig. 9-2.)

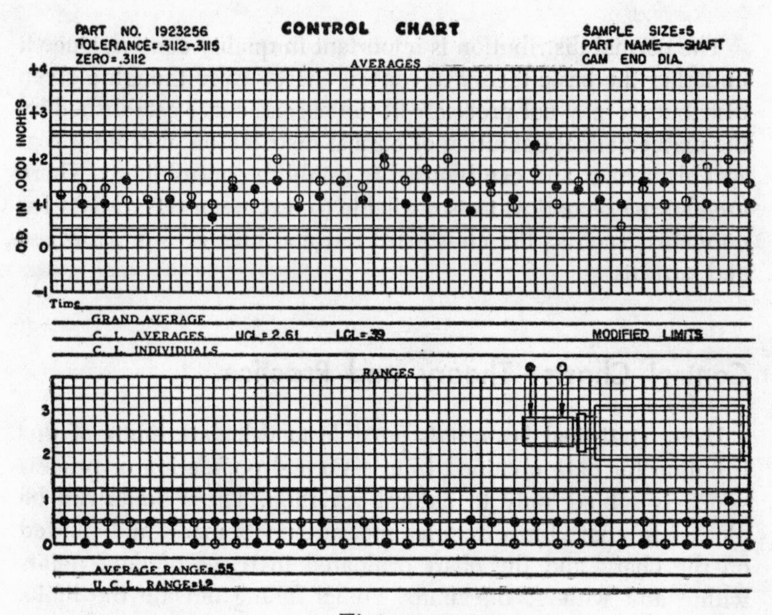

Fig. 9-2

An important distinction must be made between these two broad types of charts, based on the type of data required for each chart. On processes to be controlled by $\overline{X}$ and *R* charts, it is necessary to gather data through measurements of variation. Actual measurements of the necessary degree of precision to show variation must be taken and recorded. Go- no-go gaging cannot be used. As a result, such data is usually accumulated by a higher skilled person or more sophisticated equipment or both, and is more costly to acquire. On the other hand, the finer and more sensitive control will reduce over-all control costs in most cases.

The *p-chart* does not require actual measurements, or variables measurements. Instead, it is used to measure, in terms or percentages, the presence or absence of certain characteristics or attributes. Its measurements depend purely on counting, and are called attributes measurements. Consequently, while not as sensitive a control as the *$\overline{X}$ and R chart,* it can be used in many applications where variables measurement is impossible or impractical. For example, it can control the number of burst cartons in a truckload shipment, the number of cavities insufficiently filled in an injection molding press, etc.

It can also be used to combine several different types of defects into a single percentage reading for control purposes. There is also a special form of the *p-chart,* called the *c-chart,* which uses the number of defects found rather than the number of defectives reported. To illustrate this point, a blister and a run on a painted part are two defects for *c-chart* calculations, but the part is one defective for *p-chart* purposes.

Sampling Techniques and Tables

Sampling techniques can be developed, based on statistical studies of variability and probability, to extend quality control techniques into inspection for product acceptance, as well as for process control. Thus it is possible to use relatively small samples, yet have a scientific basis for acceptance or rejection of the product. Two further advantages of such statistical sampling over 100 per cent inspection are drastically reduced costs and more reliable data due to a lowered probability of inspector fatigue and boredom. In addition, great stress should be placed on the sorting or 100 per cent checking of rejected lots of product by the production personnel. Then, there is a great incentive encouraging the production of good product and discouraging the making of defectives. Indeed, if there is an incentive program for production workers, the incentive system should provide for either loss of incentive earnings if defective product is made, or that employees producing such material be required to sort it on "their own time."

These penalties against the individual production operator will lead to much more rapid corrective action and process improvement. No operator is going to contemplate an apparently permanent loss of earning power due to a process he cannot control and keep from producing bad work. His protests, whether to his supervision or through union channels, will provide incentive to the line organization to get quality problems (which are the responsibility of management, as distinct from the operator's problems of workmanship) straightened out.

There are only two cases where 100 per cent inspection, or sorting by the inspection function of the quality assurance organization, is justified, and should rarely occur. One is when a new product is just entering production, or when production is very limited, so that process capabilities are not yet established, control charts cannot be applied or other process control techniques used, and parts produced are too few to permit sampling. The second is when a product requirement is so critical that no defectives can be accepted and every unit must be checked. An extreme example of this is the flight test of every airplane produced, rather than the testing of a sample of aircraft.

Generally speaking, statistical sampling plans are used for acceptance or rejection of a specific lot or batch of a product. Engineers select sampling plans based on the *Operating Characteristic curve,* more commonly referred to as the *OC curve,* of each plan. (See Fig. 9-3.) This curve graphically illustrates the probability of acceptance or rejection of a lot of a certain quality level if it is inspected with a particular sampling plan. Such curves are already computed and included in the literature describing most standard sampling plans in use today.

There are two types of risks associated with the use of statistical sampling plans defined by the Operating Characteristic curve. These are the *Producer's Risk* and the *Consumer's Risk.*

The Producer's Risk This is the probability or risk of rejecting the product as a result of sampling inspection when the quality of the lot is actually acceptable. It is desirable to keep the Producer's Risk as small as possible. Every sampling plan has a certain Producer's Risk. There will be times when acceptable lots, in terms of the actual quality level, will be rejected for sorting. This loss in dollars, due to unnecessary sorting, should be greatly offset by the savings in over-all inspection costs.

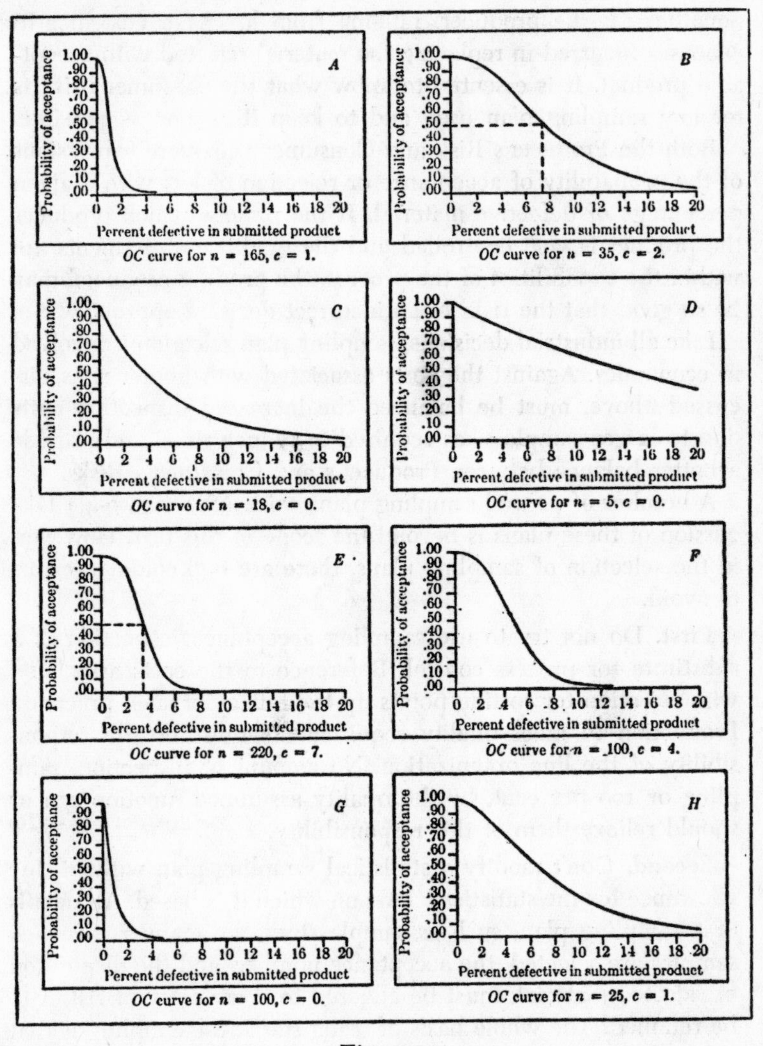

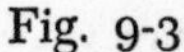
Fig. 9-3

The Consumer's Risk This is the probability or risk of accepting a product and sending it on to the consumer when the actual quality of the lot is too poor to meet the consumer's requirements. There is a strong possibility the consumer may reject the material. This possibility carries with it certain economic penalties for the producer, ranging from loss of a customer to expenses incurred in replacing the material rejected with acceptable product. It is essential to know what the consumer's risk is for any sampling plan used and to keep it as low as possible.

Both the Producer's Risk and Consumer's Risk are expressions of the probability of acceptance or rejection of lots with a given percentage of defective material. If the process which produces the product is well controlled and the quality requirements are within the capabilities of the process, the product produced may be so good that the risks of an incorrect decision approach zero.

Like all industrial decisions, sampling plan selection is involved in economics. Against the costs associated with higher risks discussed above, must be balanced the increased inspection costs due to larger sample sizes required to reduce risks, and provide a better balance between Producer's and Consumer's Risks.

A number of proved sampling plans exist. (See Fig. 9-4.) Discussion of these plans is beyond the scope of this text. However, in the selection of sampling plans, there are two common errors to avoid.

First. Do not try to use sampling acceptance inspection as a substitute for process control. Reference to the costs associated with rejection for sorting points up the fallacy of such practices. Production to meet quality requirements must be the responsibility of the line organization. No amount of inspection, sampling or 100 per cent, by the quality assurance function can or should relieve them of this responsibility.

Second. Don't modify a statistical sampling plan without due allowance for the statisticals laws on which it is based. All details of a sampling plan, such as sample sizes, the manner in which samples are selected, the acceptance number, and the disposition of rejected material, must be adhered to if certainty of risk is to be retained. The whole basis of using statistical sampling is that the probability of accepting or rejecting lots of a particular quality level is known. Careless tinkering with the plan, usually in an attempt to further reduce inspection costs, will destroy that certainty, and may increase total quality costs enormously.

AQL SAMPLING TABLE

TABLE IV-A. Master Table for Normal and Tightened Inspection (single sampling)

Sample Size Code Letter	Sample Size	Acceptable Quality Levels (normal inspection)—in percent												
		0.015	0.035	0.065	0.10	0.15	0.25	0.40	0.65	1.0	1.5	2.5	4.0	6.5
		Ac Re	Ac Re	Ac Re	Ac Re	Ac Re	Ac Re	Ac Re	Ac Re	Ac Re	Ac Re	Ac Re	Ac Re	Ac Re
A	2	↓	↓	↓	↓	↓	↓	↓	↓	↓	↓	↓	↓	↓
B	3	↓	↓	↓	↓	↓	↓	↓	↓	↓	↓	↓	↓	0 1
C	5	↓	↓	↓	↓	↓	↓	↓	↓	↓	↓	↓	0 1	↕
D	7	↓	↓	↓	↓	↓	↓	↓	↓	↓	↓	0 1	↕	↕
E	10	↓	↓	↓	↓	↓	↓	↓	↓	↓	0 1	↕	↕	1 2
F	15	↓	↓	↓	↓	↓	↓	↓	↓	0 1	↕	↕	1 2	2 3
G	25	↓	↓	↓	↓	↓	↓	↓	0 1	↕	↕	*1 2	2 3	3 4
H	35	↓	↓	↓	↓	↓	↓	0 1	↕	↕	1 2	†2 3	3 4	5 6
I	50	↓	↓	↓	↓	↓	0 1	↕	↕	1 2	2 3	3 4	4 5	6 7
J	75	↓	↓	↓	↓	0 1	↕	↕	1 2	2 3	3 4	4 5	6 7	9 10
K	110	↓	↓	↓	0 1	↕	↕	1 2	2 3	3 4	4 5	6 7	8 9	12 13
L	150	↓	↓	0 1	↕	↕	1 2	2 3	3 4	4 5	5 6	8 9	11 12	17 18
M	225	↓	0 1	↕	↕	1 2	2 3	3 4	4 5	5 6	8 9	11 12	17 18	24 25
N	300	0 1	↕	↕	1 2	2 3	3 4	4 5	5 6	7 8	10 11	14 15	20 21	32 33
O	450	↕	↕	1 2	2 3	3 4	4 5	5 6	7 8	10 11	14 15	20 21	29 30	43 44
P	750	↕	1 2	2 3	3 4	4 5	6 7	8 9	11 12	15 16	20 21	31 32	45 46	68 69
Q	1500	1 2	2 3	3 4	5 6	7 8	9 10	13 14	18 19	25 26	35 36	56 57	81 82	124 125
		0.035	0.065	0.10	0.15	0.25	0.40	0.65	1.0	1.5	2.5	4.0	6.5	10.0
		Acceptable Quality Levels (tightened inspection)—in percent												

* This is Plan H.
† This is Plan B.

Fig. 9-4

Design of Experiments

It is generally accepted that scientific discovery is not accidental, but results from planned, methodical investigation and experiment. What is not understood is the vast volume of problems inherent in experimenting and drawing reliable conclusions from experimental data. Experiments, too, are subject to variation. It is very difficult to control all elements of an experiment so that only controlled variations of certain desired elements occur. Many variations in ordinary experiments in industrial applications may lead to certain dangerous conditions such as:

1. Simple, unsophisticated analysis of experimental data may lead to misleading or incorrect conclusions.
2. This in turn may result in future experiments being channeled into wrong paths, with much waste of time and money.
3. Many of the experimental results may seem to be mysterious or unexplainable. The repetition of an experiment may not yield the same results, or results conflict with knowledge acquired from previous experiments or through shop practice.

There are methods available to design experiments and analyze the results on a statistical basis. Specific details on the methodology of statistical experiment design is beyond the scope of this text, but such work can be done and has an important place in the total quality assurance function. Some of the advantages of this statistical application are:

1. It saves valuable technical time and money.
2. Statistical methods are available to analyze data from nonrepeating experiments, drop out the effects of unwanted variations, and reconcile experimental results which conflict with previously acquired knowledge.
3. Experiments can be scheduled and controlled more precisely, and completed in less time. In the case of experiments

demanding the use of factory facilities, this is a prime consideration to prevent excessive loss of production.

No amount of statistical design or analysis, however, will improve or salvage a poorly conceived experiment. Before experimentation starts, be sure the problem has been precisely defined. *What is the objective of the experiment? Who will utilize the results, and how? How long will the experiment take, and how much time, talent and money can be expended on it? Finally, have all interested parties been consulted to insure that the needs of each are met, and have any disinterested persons with knowledge and experience to contribute to the experiment been approached?*

Process Capability

In a Process Capability study, the total variation of a process is analyzed, usually by use of control charts, into normal and nonnormal components. Then the nonnormal component is studied to determine its causes and permit measures to be taken to remove these causes from the process. In effect, an experiment is designed to yield certain specific information on the causes of the nonnormal variations. Elimination of this step removes the basic reason for undertaking Process Capabilities studies, which is to improve the processes studied.

Process Capability is not limited to shop applications. In addition to quality studies in the factory, it can be applied to administrative areas of cost control, clerical errors, office machine operation, maintenance operations, scheduling studies, etc. It can be applied to any problem which involves the study of the nature and behavior of a distribution.

A process capability study consists of four steps:

1. Perform an experiment to collect data from the process at several different points in time.
2. Review the data to determine if the process is stable, subject to nonnormal variations, and postulate a hypothesis about the process.

3. Prepare a control chart, or charts, to test the hypothesis.
4. Depending on the results, further tests through additional experimentation may now be required, and the cycle is repeated.

It is not unusual for an initial process control study to set off a seemingly unending chain of studies and experiments. This is nothing to be discouraged about, since the problems being discovered in the process or product may have been there for years. These problems will not be resolved overnight, but will require hard study over a period of weeks or months, and may result in truly basic questioning of engineering and design standards and procedures in the company.

Tolerance Analysis

One of the areas certain to be explored as a result of a process capability studies program will be engineering practices in establishing tolerances. Sooner or later, processes will be found which produce a natural distribution too wide to fit within the limits of the applicable specification. There are only three steps that can be taken to resolve this conflict:

1. Change the process,
2. Change the specification, or
3. Accept the situation and provide for 100 per cent sort and repair or scrapping of product falling outside the specification limits.

This last is not usually acceptable, except in rare cases when the process is pressing the state of the art and the specification must be maintained. Generally speaking, the first attempt will be to change the process, with consideration to cost problems that will possibly arise. If this involves excessive cost penalties, the tolerances should be reviewed. In this review it should be remembered that the natural in-control process spread should not exceed two thirds of the specified tolerances, or the drift that every process is subject to will cause occasional production of defectives. To assure minimum manufacturing costs, tolerances should be as wide as the product will accept, rather than as narrow as the shop can produce.

There are certain statistical laws which can be used to arrive at economical solutions. Every assembly involving the joining together of two or more parts also involves the mating of series of frequency distributions. The distributions of the dimensions of one component are mated with the distributions of a second part which, in turn, are joined to a third, etc. Thus it is possible to consider the use of overlapping tolerances since it can be statistically demonstrated that random assemblies can be held to narrower spreads than would be indicated by simple totaling of the dimensional spreads of the parts. Reference to any good book on statistics will provide abundant mathematical proof of this statement, as well as instructions for computing assembly tolerances and detail component tolerances.

There are certain dangers in careless application of such tolerances. First, it is essential that process capabilities be known, and that these known distributions be used as the basis of assembly tolerance calculations, rather than blueprint dimensions. Second, assembly must be based on a random selection of components, rather than sequential selection. In fact, at times it may be necessary to intermix lots of components to insure randomness since, during short intervals of time, processes do not produce the full random range of variation. For this reason, stress must be placed on field service or replacement implications, so that customers will not receive parts that do not fit in the product.

CHAPTER TEN

Measuring Results

Total Quality Assurance must report results of its activities to management in useful form for evaluation purposes at regularly scheduled intervals.

How to Report Results

The design of a reporting system begins with deciding what is required and how the system should be structured to help improve the situation it is reporting about.

Determination must also be made as to the scope and detail coverage of the reporting system. This must be based on an analysis of the systems outputs required by management for decision making, corrective action, or historical reference. Thus, the design of the reporting system breaks down into four steps:

1. A problem exists which could be corrected or prevented if management had appropriate and timely information.
2. A plan is developed based on the purpose or type of report desired.

3. A report format is designed to fit these needs.
4. Input requirements for the report are determined and provision made for the data to be supplied. This data must be accurate, timely, and adequate.

Reporting methods determination is no less important than reporting problem definition. It is the failure in this area which generally causes complaints about "lack of system" in quality assurance reports. At this point, decisions must be made as to the methods of collecting data and processing it. Shall it be clerical or mechanized? What formats are to be used? How can we minimize inspector and engineer effort through appropriate form design to cut data-posting time? Shall codes be used? How can the impact of clerical errors be minimized?

There is no single report form which is correct for all applications. Each report must be developed for the particular application, and thought should be given to the following:

1. Information must be fed back accurately and rapidly.

2. Information gathered for control purposes is of value only if it is fed back to its source or its point of control.

3. The principle of exception reporting must be followed. Bulky, detailed reports are never justified for management use.

4. Consider application of sampling techniques and control limits to report preparation.

5. Use selective distribution. People should receive reports only if they are responsible for or control the function.

6. Choose report indicators carefully. The best is always the dollar—that universal parameter of management control.

7. Use graphical or pictorial presentation techniques liberally to improve reader interest and understanding. (See Fig. 10-1.)

8. Discriminate between periodic reports for standing control purposes and special reports for particular problems.

9. Check reports prior to distribution for clarity and accuracy. If possible, have a quality assurance technical person who was not involved in preparation of the report review it for ease of understanding and freedom from problems of conflicting interpretations.

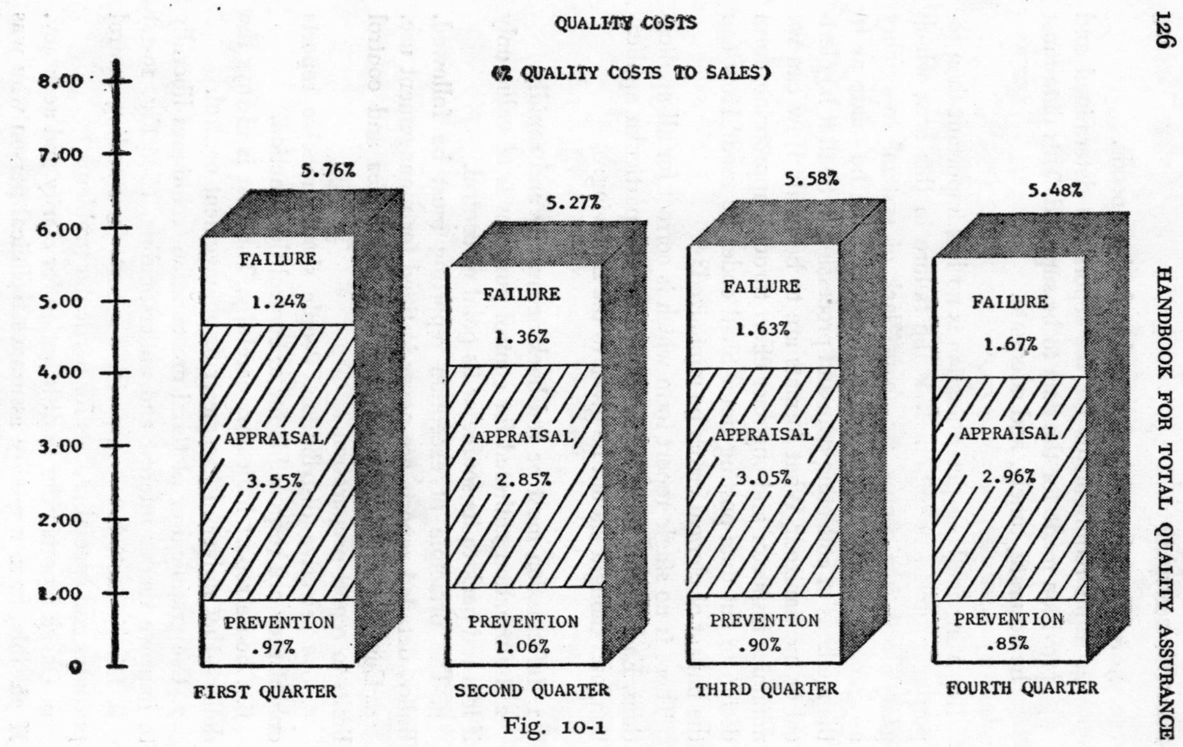
QUALITY COSTS
(% QUALITY COSTS TO SALES)
PERCENT TO SALES
8.00
7.00
6.00
5.00
4.00
3.00
2.00
1.00
0
5.76%
FAILURE
1.24%
APPRAISAL
3.55%
PREVENTION
.97%
FIRST QUARTER
5.27%
FAILURE
1.36%
APPRAISAL
2.85%
PREVENTION
1.06%
SECOND QUARTER
5.58%
FAILURE
1.63%
APPRAISAL
3.05%
PREVENTION
.90%
THIRD QUARTER
5.48%
FAILURE
1.67%
APPRAISAL
2.96%
PREVENTION
.85%
FOURTH QUARTER

Fig. 10-1

10. Assign responsibility for control and correction in the report. If a problem is highlighted, show to whom it belongs.

11. Audit the report system continuously for cost reduction, effectiveness, distribution, and degree of reliance by recipients. Ruthlessly weed out unneeded copies or obsolete reports.

Evaluation of Personnel

There are two types of quality assurance personnel—the thinkers and the doers. Like all oversimplifications, this is not quite accurate but, in general, the evaluation of inspectors and their first-level supervision is, and must be, on a different scale than the evaluation of the quality control engineers and the quality assurance managerial staff.

Quality assurance results are the product of the people employed in the function. Therefore, to measure quality assurance results, one must measure personnel effectiveness and act on these evaluations, either by additional training, reassignment, or replacement of substandard people. The quality assurance manager who flinches from these tasks is not effective. Also he is penalizing his people who, unaware of their mistakes, continue to compound them.

The following check list of personnel performance factors is useful in evaluation work:

DOERS	THINKERS	PRESENT CAPABILITIES
X	X	**INITIATIVE**—a self-starter, alert for situations requiring action, confident of his ability to think things through himself.
X	X	**DEPENDABILITY**—persistent, determined to get the job done, reliable in following through and completing assignments.
X	X	**JUDGMENT**—considering all pertinent factors, making decisions quickly but carefully, and accepting responsibility for his decisions.
X	X	**COOPERATIVENESS**—a team player, open-minded and flexible, adapting

		easily and accepting new ideas quickly.
X	X	**EMOTIONAL STABILITY**—self-controlled, accepting criticism constructively, and working wtih people at all levels in all functions with an air of competence, confidence, and optimism.
X		**ORGANIZING ABILITY**—working out systematic methods of handling routine operations and not being overwhelmed with details.
X	X	**LEARNING ABILITY**—grasping verbal and written instructions quickly and, by working both on and off the job, increasing his personal knowledge and effectiveness.
X	X	**RESPONSIBILITY**—handling assignments in his immediate jurisdiction and accepting without hesitation assignments outside his immediate area of responsibility.
	X	**PERSUASIVENESS**—expressing ideas so that others give support, interest, and willing cooperation.
	X	**CREATIVENESS**—visualizing new and novel approaches to old problems, welcoming and assisting in change, and pressing forward into new fields.
X		**LEADERSHIP**—ability to create "esprit de corps" by understanding and showing a real regard for the dreams, feelings, and aspirations of those around him, giving credit where credit is due, and a full realization of the role of high morale in successful operations.
	X	**REALISTIC HUMILITY**—the willingness to subordinate personal pride and public recognition needs to the greater goal of getting the job done by passing such rewards on to others who also participated.

DOERS	THINKERS	PERFORMANCE APPRAISAL
X		**PRODUCTIVITY AND COST**—uses manpower, equipment, and supplies properly to meet schedules with maximum productivity at lowest immediate and long-range costs, and within budget and labor standards.
X	X	**PLANNING AND SCHEDULING**—plans and schedules his subordinates' work, and his own job, so that commitments are met without undue overtime, including his own.
X	X	**CONTROLS**—plans for and uses effective controls to assure action is taken as required, information is distributed and utilized, and discrepancies from plans are accounted for.
X	X	**DISCIPLINE**—maintain discipline and order fairly but firmly through equitable handling of employee problems, but without compromising his own or the company's position.
X		**HOUSEKEEPING**—work areas are kept as neat and clean as possible, compatible with completion of jobs in process and preparation for future jobs.
X	X	**PERFORMANCE IMPROVEMENT**—Works on and executes a continuous program to improve total job performance, both of his group and of himself, and contributes to efforts by others to improve.

DOERS	THINKERS	METHODS UTILIZATION
X	X	**COMMUNICATIONS**—keeps himself, his subordinates, superiors, and associates informed of significant occurrences on a timely basis.
X	X	**POLICIES AND PROCEDURES**—is informed of and follows company policies and procedures and sees

		that others working with him also comply with them.
X		**SAFETY**—works safely himself, and demands that those working with him do likewise.
X	X	**EMPLOYEE RELATIONS**—treats employees as individuals and wins their support both for himself as their superior and for the company who employs them.
X	X	**TRAINING**—insures continual training and development of employees under his supervision to keep abreast of changing job assignments and technologies and to develop to maximum potential for promotion.

In evaluating personnel, the basic concern is the contribution made by each individual toward realization of the company goals or the total quality assurance function. What counts are the results obtained through the employment of each individual in his present specific assignment. Consideration must also be given to the future potential that a person has in the organization. If the employee is not presently contributing, then it should be recognized that the entire cost of his employment must be charged against whatever future utilization is planned of this person's services. Often this bill can be quite high.

Objective and Program Review

Results are measured in terms of the success with which program objectives have been realized. Each program can be measured by the following three factors:

1. **Effectiveness of program.**
   Reduction in defectives.
   Increase in production yield.
   Reduction in customer complaints.
   Changes in quality audit scores.
   Changes in vendor or other quality ratings.

2. **Efficiency of execution.**
   Adherence to program schedule.
   Adherence to program budget.
   Losses experienced by other departments as a result of program operation.

3. **Costs relative to savings.**
   Salaries, wages, and other expenses incurred.
   Savings realized in direct and indirect labor and material.
   Cost/savings ratio in dollars.
   Cost/quality improvement ratio in rating changes or other indexes.
   Scrap and salvage cost reductions.
   Warranty and customer claim cost reductions.
   Sales increases attributable to quality programs.

PROFIT—THE YARDSTICK FOR RESULTS

In evaluating the results of total quality assurance operations, it must be possible to equate results to dollars, and prove that a contribution is being made to the future of the business. If this contribution is lacking, drastic changes will then be made in the quality assurance program.

Head them off! Plan and program in terms of dollars, report to management in terms of dollars, and insure management's favorable evaluation of the results of total quality assurance. If management requires assistance in reaching such an evaluation, it means the reports are too complex and fail to achieve desired results.

CHAPTER ELEVEN

Tomorrow's Master Plan Concept

The June, 1963, issue of *Factory* magazine contained an editorial on the lowly beer can. The editor described the rapid evolution of beer can design during a period of a few months, after more than twenty years without change or innovation. This was cited as an outstanding example of a breakthrough where none seemed possible.

So it is with quality assurance. We have reviewed its development, from early inspection practices to statistical quality control to its present state, which included all aspects of a business as a basic operating philosophy. What of the future? Certainly there are more changes and innovations to come in this field.

Any quality assurance function has the following three choices with regard to improvement.

First. It can stand pat, convinced that its present techniques and practices are the best required and will not require change. This is not a sound approach, unless employed in a company created for a specific job, and to be abolished when the job is completed. A good example is one of the joint ventures set up to build a specific highway or dam. Then it is foolish to waste money and resources in experimenting with innovation.

Second. A firm may elect to stay alert to innovations in its field and copy those which are applicable to its endeavors. There are two flaws in this procedure: (1) copying does not always guarantee properly grasping and correctly applying the innovation and its use may cause more harm than good; (2) one's competitors are being granted a considerable advantage in time, since a copyist is months or years behind the originator in reaping the full returns from a change.

Third. A firm may actively work at changing quality assurance practices and methods, in addition to remaining in constant touch with the field to obtain the best of others' work. Over the long run, this choice will be the most fruitful, because the drive for innovation will result in a more critical scanning of the literature and quality practices of others, with a consequent greater yield than obtained under the second method.

The Master Plan Concept

The quality manager must plan and program for long-term improvement. In planning he must recognize the fact that management is not prepared to accept all of the changes and innovations he wants to make. On the other hand, in the press of day-to-day operations, the quality manager may forget and take action which may imperil his long-term objectives. Therefore, he must plan ahead, and consider what these long-term objectives are.

The development of long-term objectives is a team effort because no single person can grasp all the implications and ramifications of a job as complex as total quality assurance. Also cross-checking by other participants in the give-and-take of idea development will prevent building many unforeseen errors into the master plan.

Caution is necessary in selecting planning assistants. A prime requisite for selection is the ability to keep one's mouth shut. The criteria for selection should not be based on a man's organizational position, but rather on the size and clarity of the contribution he can make. The quality manager must also recognize that the men he selects will become members of the operation's "inner circle" and give careful thought to all the implications.

Out of this thought, planning, and consultation develops a "master plan" to define the organization, objectives and operating procedures of the quality assurance function a specific number of years hence, disregarding obstacles which at present prevent this plan from becoming an immediate reality. The plan does not have to be typewritten and elaborately illustrated with charts. A single hand-written copy will suffice. It is essential that it be in an understandable form, easily accessible to the quality assurance manager and his key assistants. It should be used as a daily reference in guiding operating decisions so that steady progress is made to bring the plan into reality.

By using a single copy, it will then be easier to keep the plan current by incorporating modifications which internal experience and outside contacts indicate are needed. It is also safer because it will contain frank and controversial statements which may be violently opposed by individuals outside the quality assurance function. For that reason, it is wise to keep the master plan under lock and key.

The quality management of one heavy-equipment manufacturer referred to its master plan book as the "shadow plan." This definition illustrates the need for discretion and also illustrates the use of such a plan to foreshadow coming events.

Development of Strategy

There is certain to be many obstacles to overcome in putting the master plan into operation. Therefore, in long-range quality improvements it is necessary to determine precisely what these obstacles are and to define them as accurately as possible. They should be noted in the master plan, and means considered to combat each obstacle. For example, one of the objectives in the master plan of a machinery manufacturer was to:

Convert engineering drawing dimensioning practices to the use of datum plane, nonaccumulative tolerances, and open dimension chains.

The first obstacle was:

The vice president of engineering did not believe in such practices!

This was a formidable hurdle, but ways were planned to bypass it. As a first step the quality manager took an active interest in the industry trade association and its standards committee. It was frequently necessary to seek the vice president's permission to use his people in committee work, particularly in developing engineering definitions as industry standards. Naturally, the vice president was flattered and in due time developed an urge to participate himself. An invitation was obtained for him to serve on a panel discussion on engineering practices. During this discussion, at the association's national meeting, a floor question led to talk about dimensioning standards used by the companies of panel members. This aroused a great amount of interest and the vice president was noticeably more open-minded on the subject when he returned home.

This Machiavellian approach took two years to mature. Every step, including the question from the floor at the meeting, was planned. Great care was taken throughout the process not to embarrass or antagonize the executive who was the target. The program worked! Therefore, when you hear that something can't be done because the engineers oppose it, the question to ask is: What is being done to persuade them to change their minds?

As each obstacle is plotted and strategy developed to overcome it, a timetable should be established and written into the master plan document. The plan then becomes an outline for future quality improvement and a schedule for its attainment.

Tactics

Half a loaf is better than none. True, particularly in Quality Assurance, if you can plan and hope to get the other half of the loaf at some future date. In the meantime be sure you do not lose what you already have. Day-to-day operations on the firing line must avoid imperiling the long-run objectives. This involves the following tactical considerations:

1. **Avoid antagonizing people you need as allies over the long haul.** It may often be necessary to intentionally surrender a strong point if winning it would create too much friction.
2. **Limit the number of organizational components you battle at any one time.** It is very hard to convince most people, including the boss, that you alone are right and the rest of the world is wrong.
3. **When you decide to fight, win!** Don't get embroiled in organizational conflicts that you're going to lose. It's too hard on prestige and will cost you future support. Nobody wants to side with a loser.
4. **Don't carry fights outside the company.** Whatever else you do, don't weep in everybody's beer when you do lose one.
5. **Be certain your people know what they are doing and are sure of their facts.** Support your subordinates and in return they owe you accurate and timely data. Run a periodic check on the accuracy of the information you receive from your people.

Evaluation of Progress

The master plan and its schedules should be reviewed weekly or monthly to determine if all is well, or if new concepts, obstacles, or delays necessitate changes. Death or resignation of key people, major changes in the company's markets or products, or technological breakthroughs may require revamping part or all of the plan.

One business machine manufacturer employs 280 people in its quality assurance operation. Its master plan includes a five-year forecast of personnel and training requirements. In this five-year span, it is estimated that 221 additional quality assurance people will be required to support the forecasted growth of the company, and 350 people to replace losses during the same period. A total of 571 persons must be selected, hired, trained and put to work in the next 1,250 working days, or one person every two working days. Obviously, any change in the estimated attrition or growth rates will require major adjustments in this master plan.

Such changes must be faithfully incorporated in the plan. A master plan which is not kept current is useless. This is another reason why the number of copies, and the circulation should be restricted.

Total quality assurance can be applied in any business concern by a determined management. Properly planned and implemented, it will make a major contribution to the profitability and survival of the firm, through reduction in quality costs and increases in the reputation and salability of the company's products. It is a powerful business tool which cannot be ignored in these competitive times.

Selected Bibliography

Quality Assurance Methodology

The two standard texts in the field of statistical quality control which every quailty assurance specialist should be familiar with are:

Grant, E. L., *Statistical Quality Control,* McGraw-Hill Book Company, New York, 1952.

Shewhart, W. A., *Economic Control of Quality of Manufactured Product,* D. Van Nostrand Co., Inc., New York, 1931. (Out of print but available in most technical libraries.)

General Statistics

There are also a number of texts on business statistics in general which are helpful in developing a general understanding of the subject. These are:

Reinke, William A., *Statistics for Decision Making,* National Foremen's Institute, Waterford, Conn., 1963.

Dean, B. V., Sasieni, M. W., and Gupta, S. K., *Mathematics for Modern Management,* John Wiley and Sons, New York, 1963.

Fowler, F. P., Jr., and Sandburg, E. W., *Basic Mathematics for Administration,* John Wiley and Sons, New York, 1962.

Howell, J. E., and Teichroew, D., *Mathematical Analysis for Business Decisions*, Richard D. Irwin, Inc., Homewood, Ill., 1963.

Meier, R. C., and Archer, S. H., *An Introduction to Mathematics for Business Analysis*, McGraw-Hill Book Co., 1960.

Stern, M. E., *Mathematics for Management*, Prentice-Hall, Inc., Englewood Cliffs, N. J., 1963.

Of the many books on statistical quality control techniques and theories, the following have been selected for complete coverage:

American Society for Testing Materials, *Manual on Quality Control of Materials*, Philadelphia, 1951.

American Standards Association, *Control Chart Method of Controlling Quality During Production*, Washington, D. C., 1950.

Bowker, A. H., and Goode, H. P., *Sampling Inspection by Variables*, McGraw-Hill Book Co., Inc., 1952.

Burr, I. W., *Engineering Statistics and Quality Control*, McGraw-Hill Book Co., Inc., 1953.

Chorafas, D., *Statistical Processes and Reliability Engineering*, D. Van Nostrand Co., Inc., New York, 1960.

Cowden, D. J., *Statistical Methods in Quality Control*, Prentice-Hall, Inc., Englewood Cliffs, N. J., 1957.

Duncan, A. J., *Quality Control and Industrial Statistics*, Richard D. Irwin, Homewood, Ill., 1953.

Enrick, N. L., *Quality Control*, The Industrial Press, New York, 1954.

Hald, A., *Statistical Theory With Engineering Applications*, John Wiley and Sons, New York, 1952.

Heide, John D., *Industrial Process Control by Statistical Methods*, McGraw-Hill Book Co., Inc., New York, 1952.

Mood, A. M., and Graybill, F. A., *Introduction to the Theory of Statistics*, McGraw-Hill Book Co., Inc., New York, 1963.

Schrock, E. M., *Quality Control and Statistical Methods*, 2nd. Ed., Reinhold, New York, 1957.

Wallis, A. A., and Roberts, H. V., *Statistics: A New Approach*, The Free Press, Glencoe, Ill., 1956.

Young, H. D., *Statistical Treatment of Experimental Data*, McGraw-Hill Book Co., Inc., New York, 1962.

Management Techniques

The two standards in the field of general quality assurance management are:

Feigenbaum, A. V., *Total Quality Control*, McGraw-Hill Book Co., Inc., 1961.

Juran, J. M., *Quality Control Handbook*, 2nd. Ed., McGraw-Hill Book Co., Inc., New York, 1961.

About the Author

Edward M. Stiles is Quality Assurance Manager of the Olivetti-Underwood Corporation, in Hartford, Connecticut, where he is responsible for all quality assurance, quality control, reliability, and inspection functions and quality liaison with overseas sales and manufacturing affiliates.

Prior to joining Underwood in 1961, Mr. Stiles was Quality Control Manager and Production Manager with Bucyrus-Erie Company; had varied manufacturing assignments with the Ford Motor Company; was a Senior Methods Engineer at the John Deere Des Moines Works of Deere and Company; and Production Coordinator for Joseph Weidenhoff, Incorporated.

Mr. Stiles attended the University of Iowa, the United States Military Academy at West Point, and is a senior member of the American Society for Quality Control and the Society of Automotive Engineers. He has lectured extensively on Quality Assurance at management seminars.

INDEX